Classic Cowboy Songs

To Imogene
Best Wishes
Don Edwards
Oct '99

CLASSIC

Cowboy Songs

from the Minstrel of the Range

DON EDWARDS

As a lively ~~father~~
conversationist
She is the queen
Here's to my buddy - Imogene -
Love Rich

GIBBS·SMITH
P
PUBLISHER

SALT LAKE CITY

The Bob Nolan song lyrics "Old Home Town," found on pages 18-19, are used by permission of Garrett Music Enterprises, © 1979 Peso Music, Royse City, Texas.

"The Road Not Taken," found in the Introduction on page 20, is taken from the book *The Poetry of Robert Frost,* edited by Edward Connery Lathem and published by Henry Holt & Co.

The Gail Gardner, Don Edwards, and Paul C. Stone song "Cowboy Love Song," found on pages 44-45, is used by permission of CPP / Belwin, Inc., Miami, Florida. Copyright © 1935 (renewed) EMI Robbins Catalog Inc. All rights reserved.

"The Long Road West," found on pages 74-75, is from *Songs of the Trail* by Henry Herbert Knibbs. Copyright © 1920 by Henry Herbert Knibbs.. Copyright © renewed 1948 by Ida Julia Knibbs.. Reprinted by permission of Houghton Miffin Co. All rights reserved. Performance rights not included.

The James Grafton Rogers poem "Longside the Santa Fe Trail," found on pages 76-77, was originally penned in 1911. The Music is traditional.

The R. W. Hampton song "Travelin' Light," found on pages 114-15, is used by permission.

The Huddie Ledbetter (Leadbelly) song "When I Was a Cowboy," found on pages 120-21, was collected and adapted by John A. Lomax and Alan Lomax. TRO © 1936 (Renewed) Folkways Music Publishers, Inc., New York, New York. Used by permission.

First Edition

97 96 95 94   10 9 8 7 6 5 4 3 2 1

Copyright ©1994 Don Edwards

This is a Peregrine Smith Book, published by
Gibbs Smith, Publisher
P.O. Box 667
Layton, Utah 84041

J. Scott Knudsen, designer
Madge Baird, editor
Linda Nimori, editor
Smiley Irvin, front and back cover photos

Printed and bound in the United States of America

Library of Congress Cataloging-in-Publication Data

Classic cowboy songs / from Don Edwards.
    p. of music
    Folk songs melodies with chord symbols and guitar chord diagrams.
    ISBN 0-87905-605-3 (hard).—ISBN 0-87905-617-7 (pbk.)
    1. Cowboys—West (U.S.)—Songs and music. 2. Folk music—West (U.S.) 3. Folk songs, English—West (U.S.) I. Edwards, Don.
II. Title: 50 favorite cowboy songs. III. Title: Fifty favorite cowboy songs.
M1629.6.W5C53   1994   94-1774
                                                              CIP
                                                               M

This book is dedicated to the memory of my father John and my daughter Dayle—
for whom I wish I had given more of myself;

to my mother, Eugenie, and Mary Davis—for their love and encouragement;

to my wonderful daughters Courtney and Llayne—
for their love and understanding of my cowboy ways;

and to my beloved wife, Kathy, without whose help with this book
and my life in general, I would be plumb out of luck.

Don gets loving support from his wife, Kathy (upper right), hugs his two moms—Kathy's mother, Mary, and Don's mother, Eugenie (upper left)—spends time with his oldest daughter, Llayne (left), and prepares to "give away" his daughter Courtney on her wedding day, February 26, 1993 (below).

Contents

Preface

It was once said that to tell the cowboy's story was to sing his songs. The songs of the cowboy were songs about his life, passed by oral tradition from cow camp to bunkhouse. The singing helped to blanket the lonesomeness and to keep a rider awake while riding night guard. For the most part, the music was just whistling and humming to let the restless herd know of the cowboy's presence.

> *My trusty little night horse, he's gentle and smart;*
> *He's heard my songs so much,*
>> *he knows 'em by heart—*
> *The creak of the saddle, a loose bridle rein,*
> *His hoofs keepin' time to "Poor Liza Jane."*[1]

Nathan Howard "Jack" Thorp was the first to systematically gather and publish a collection of cowboy songs. One night, in a camp he had ridden up on some forty-five miles below Roswell, New Mexico, Jack heard a black cowhand by the name of "Lasses" sing a song called "Dodgin' Joe." Jack decided to take time out of his job on the Bar W Ranch at Carrizozo, New Mexico, to start hunting cowboy songs.

> *Long ago there was a man*
>> *who rode throughout the West*
> *Collecting songs and poetry and verses of the range.*
> *He wrote "Little Joe, the Wrangler"*
>> *and "The Pecos River Queen";*
> *A ballad-huntin' cowboy,*
>> *and Jack Thorp was his name.*[2]

"Cowboys didn't just sing cowboy songs," said Jack. "A lot of singin' on the range had nothing to do with cowboy songs as such. They sang everything from railroad songs to sentimental ballads. Cowboys weren't always singing about 'little dogies' or 'give me a home where the buffalo roam.'"

Most of the songs came from Ireland, Scotland, England, and western Europe, where the cowboys borrowed traditional ballads and sea chanties and changed them into their own songs to fit their surroundings. Many of their songs were made into parodies too bawdy to print. Remember, these were the days when men didn't cuss around women and children, only among themselves.

The oral tradition mostly disappeared with the coming of recorded music. The first commercially recorded cowboy song was Bentley Ball's Columbia recording of "The Dying Cowboy" in 1919, followed by Charles Nabell's 1924 recording of "The Great Roundup" for OKEH Records. The first successful recording of a genuine cowboy song, "When the Work's All Done This Fall," was recorded by Carl T. Sprague in 1925 and sold nearly one million records. These were soon followed with the recordings of Jules Verne Allen, Otto Gray and his Oklahoma Cowboys, and Buster Coward and The Tune Wranglers from San Antonio, Texas. All these men were actual working cowboys not too far removed from the open range, who had gone on to be popular entertainers and recording artists.

The written or composed songs of Jimmie Rodgers, Bob Nolan, Billy Hill, and Cindy Walker celebrated the beauty of the West and the love of living close to nature. They never claimed to be cowboys, but they knew and loved the West that they wrote about.

> *In the evening's twilight, melancholy shadows stray*
> *Down the trail of memories*
>> *from West of Yesterday.*[3]

By the mid-1960s, the singing cowboys of stage, radio, silver screen, and phonograph records were rapidly disappearing. In the minds of most Americans, the music died when the open range passed into history, along with the demise of the B-western film. Cowboy and western music had gone over the Great Divide. Marty Robbins's gunfighter songs were still fairly popular, but, for the most part, cowboy and western music was gone, unless you were fortunate enough to hear Glenn Ohrlin or Rambling Jack Elliott at a folk festival or on a college campus somewhere. While singer/songwriters and folk music in general were still popular, no one seemed to care about cowboy songs, the music indigenous to the West, especially in Texas and California where the cowboy had his earliest and deepest roots. It did resurface briefly in the mid-1970s. Then came the near fatal blow— The Urban Cowboy Craze of the greedy '80s. But this pseudo-cowboy fad mercifully died a quick death.

The range is a changing into neon and noise,
And folks have lost touch with the land.
They may tap their feet to an old cowboy song,
But mostly they don't understand.[4]

Then in 1985 came heaven's blessing from the high sagebrush desert of northeastern Nevada. Cowboys from all over the West were coming to Elko for the first annual Cowboy Poetry Gathering. This single event, one of the largest of its kind, not only brought about a worldwide interest in cowboy poetry and storytelling but brought with it a renewed interest in cowboy music. Contemporary writers and singers were performing their songs about the West they loved, with lyrics and melodies that sounded as though they could have been written a hundred years ago, as well as songs lamenting a modern West being swallowed up by the government bureaucracy and greed. The remainder of the decade brought about an awareness not seen for nearly fifty years.

See him out there on the prairie alone,
A solitary cowboy from out of the past.
Riding and singing all by himself,
Of the old singing cowboys, he may be the last.[4]

Through the years, I thought maybe I was the last—the last of the cowboy minstrels who sang and told stories around the campfire or while riding night guard, their voices softly ringing like their jingle-bobbed spurs. "The Campfire Has Gone Out" and the "Chant of the Night Songs" were no more to be heard. But I never gave up, never abandoned the cowboy music in favor of the overproduced country-western style. The best music, regardless of its genre, comes from within a culture, rooted in its tradition. This is the kind of music that lasts for centuries.

Now, in the last decade of the twentieth century, there seems to be no end in sight. Since cowboy music and poetry are being released and distributed internationally on major record labels—most recently by Warner Brothers and their new subsidiary Warner/Western—others are sure to follow.

There are more and more western movies being made for television as well as the big screen. People are going back to their roots and traditional values. They want the real thing; the country is growing tired of the hype. As always during uneasy times, people look to the West, where the cowboy is the symbol of independence and self-reliance. The greatest folk hero the world has ever known is "Back in the Saddle Again."

This book is not meant to be an academic or scholarly account of cowboy and western music. It's just my own story of my life and my music—an autobiographical songbag, if you will. Over the last forty years or so, I have accumulated some two thousand songs in my repertoire. Many I still sing, while others have long since been forgotten, either intentionally or from years of neglect. In order to keep this collection down to a reasonable fifty songs, I have tried to select those songs that best represent my musical tastes and influences, while at the same time choosing songs that both young and old alike can play, sing, and enjoy.

You will find traditional cowboy songs, western songs, western swing, jazz-influenced songs, cowboy songs with early blues influence, as well as contemporary cowboy and western songs by modern writers in the old tradition. There are even songs that were not cowboy songs at all, but songs that cowboys liked to sing. These songs were written by lots of folks—some famous, some long forgotten. Some I wrote myself, while others just sort o' grew.

So don't just read this book and put it away to gather dust. You've got to use it. Just as the land will go to seed if you don't use it, so will the songs if they're corralled up in some library archive. We don't own these songs any more than we own the land. We are stewards—caretakers nurturing both the land and the music and keeping it healthy for future generations.

You got to sing 'em, play 'em, teach 'em to your kids, and pass 'em on to your friends. Then, maybe someday you'll know . . .

The feeling you get from a campfire's warm glow
As the plaintive notes of his songs softly flow—
Songs about cowboys, horses, and trains;
He's a disappearing minstrel of the range.[4]

Good luck,
Don Edwards

NOTES

1. "Chant of the Night Songs" by Don Edwards, © 1986 Night Horse Songs (BMI)

2. "The Ballad Hunter" by Don Edwards, © 1986 Night Horse Songs (BMI)

3. "West of Yesterday" by Don Edwards, ©1993 Night Horse Songs (BMI)

4. "Minstrel of the Range" by Don Edwards, ©1989 Night Horse Songs (BMI)

Acknowledgments

I wish to express my sincere thanks and appreciation to all of you who have been such a source of help and inspiration in making this book possible:

my best friend, Waddie Mitchell;

all my cowboy friends—Gary Morton, Cliff Teinert, Bob Moline, Wallace McRae, Baxter Black—who keep alive the noble traditions of the range;

my friends Hal Cannon, Paul Stone, Guy Logsdon, and Jim Bob Tinsley—for generously sharing their knowledge and wisdom;

my musical mentors Herb Hooven, Rich O'Brien, Tom Morrell, and Bob Boatright—for their many years of friendship and enriching our lives with their gift of music;

Joe Dulle—for being the first with the idea to present the "Cowboy Campfire Concert"; and my friends Steve Murrin and Paul McCallum—for believing in "The Hundred Year Deal" (it's finally coming true);

my longtime friends Ray Self, Bob Coffey, Dick Cappleman, Larry Scott, and Ken Griffis—for their years of support and encouragement.

It would take volumes to sing the praises of all the singers, poets, authors, and cowboy heroes who have inspired me and enriched my life. It hardly seems enough to just say thanks, but I hope they know how much I appreciate them one and all:

Nathan Howard "Jack" Thorp
Tom Mix
Will James
Charles "Badger" Clark
Bob Nolan
Marty Robbins
Bob Wills
Walt LaRue
Jimmie Rodgers
Woody Guthrie
Glenn Ohrlin
Gene Autry
Rex Allen
Roy Rogers
Tex Ritter
Ray Whitley
Riders in the Sky

Introduction

S everal years ago, during one of my all-too-infrequent trips to visit my mother, we were sitting on the front porch of that wonderful old New England house in what was once a modest, middle-class neighborhood on Oak Road in Milton, Massachusetts. One evening, our conversation concerned itself with my relentless obsession with cowboys and music. She told me she hadn't given much thought to my "cowboy thing" when I was young; that was something every kid wanted to be when they were growing up. She just thought I'd outgrow it sooner or later, but, "It was all your father and I could do to get you to take off your cowboy hat and boots and get you dressed up long enough to go to church on Sunday morning."

My memories of home in Boonton, New Jersey, where I was born in 1939, include lots of aunts and uncles who visited and told me stories and sang songs. From church singing to the Saturday night dances at the Grange hall, summers there were full of music and fun.

Though I loved those singing and storytelling sessions, I have to admit I was impressed with our own new Silvertone radio and phonograph console. It was one of those fancy ones that could cut discs from radio shows and came with a microphone so you could record your own singing or whatever else you wanted to record. My dad used to record all those "Gene Autry Melody Ranch" shows for me every Sunday night. I've still got some of those old duo-discs, but most

have long since deteriorated. My dad's extensive 78rpm record collection has fared much better, I'm thankful to say, as I was heavily influenced by his eclectic tastes in music, which included everything from Bach to John Philip Sousa, from Glenn Miller to Jimmie Rodgers, and Louis Armstrong to Gene Autry. He had Carter Family records and cowboy singers like Vernon Dalhart, Jules Verne Allen, Carson Robinson and Bill Bender. He even had some Bob Wills and The Sons of the Pioneers.

There were good experiences in those growing-up days that were shaping my life, but I never gave up putting the pressure on my dad for us to move out West. I thought a time or two I had him convinced. Then one day he announced that we were going to move. He had been laid off from his job at the aircraft plant where he was an aircraft radio technician. He was just one of thousands who lost their jobs after the war was over and had to look for other means of making a living. I can recall that little twinge of excitement I felt when I thought that maybe we were going to venture out and head for Texas, Arizona, or perhaps Montana, but when my dad said, "Massachusetts," I could have died. I didn't mind the trips to visit my aunts during the summer once in a while. I kind of enjoyed the family outings at the beach. I liked the ocean—but to live there!

I always resented the change from rural life to living in town. The years after this move were my most rebellious ones, and I realize now that my behavior was totally unfair to my parents, who were doing all that was humanly possible to support the

Don shares **Christmas 1947** with his parents, John and Eugenie, and his sisters, Nancy and Judy, at their home in New Jersey (upper right). The future cowboy troubadour holds a tiple, which his dad played in his minstrel and vaudeville acts. A tiple is an Argentine folk instrument, and the word means "small guitar" in Spanish. It has ten strings and was originally tuned to guitar pitch, with later versions tuned to ukulele pitch (right).

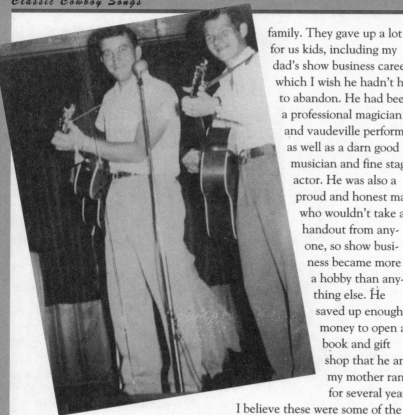

Pickin' and singin', the Shuck Brothers ("Corn" and "Cob") are actually Don and longtime friend Joe Cox (ca. 1957).

family. They gave up a lot for us kids, including my dad's show business career, which I wish he hadn't had to abandon. He had been a professional magician and vaudeville performer as well as a darn good musician and fine stage actor. He was also a proud and honest man who wouldn't take a handout from anyone, so show business became more of a hobby than anything else. He saved up enough money to open a book and gift shop that he and my mother ran for several years. I believe these were some of the happiest times for them. There's no better feeling than being self-sufficient and self-reliant, knowing that the reins of success and failure are in your own hands.

But life's trail wasn't meant to be a smooth one, for a fire destroyed the store. My parents watched hopelessly as their dreams and life's savings went up in smoke. Things weren't the same after that. Dad and Mom both took jobs I know they didn't really like. They never complained about it, but we have to remember these were times when folks took care of themselves. You either worked or went hungry. No dysfunctional, woe-is-me, it's-not-my-fault crap in those days.

The family made the best of a bad situation and things went along quite normally. In fact, the Christmas of 1948 was the best Christmas in my whole life. I received my first guitar—a Sears and Roebuck Silverstone sunburst archtop—my first Will James book—*Smoky The Cow Horse*—and if that wasn't enough, my uncle Ned gave me a genuine Daisy Red Ryder BB rifle. I still have the BB rifle and the Will James book, as well as many of his other books that I received for birthdays and Christmases in the years to follow. My one regret is that I don't have the guitar anymore. I'd give almost anything to have it back, or at least one like it. Somewhere back in one of my weaker brain-dead childhood moments, I traded it for a

wore-out saddle and an old Stella flat-top—both of which I also no longer have.

I played cornet for a while in school, as well as the Hawaiian steel guitar that I wish now I had more seriously pursued—and yes, I know what you're thinking and I don't want to talk about it. I do wish I had them back, especially the steel body tri-cone National; that was a beautiful guitar. But remember I was just a stupid kid. No, I take that back, ignorance is a better word because you can fix ignorance; stupidity is fatal. Believe me, I learned the hard way. So let me pass on a little piece of advice to you aspiring musicians: don't go trading off those old instruments unless you know what you're doing. (In my own defense, there were quite a few of these instruments around in those days, and you could buy a pretty decent one fairly reasonable.) Also, don't give up playing one instrument for the sake of another. Learn as many as you can learn to play well. You'll be all the richer for your extended musical knowledge.

It took me a lot of years to finally decide to take music more seriously. It was always a main priority, but the pursuit of cowboy dreams was growing stronger. I was totally absorbed with Will James, Gene Autry, Tom Mix and the like. Most of my Saturday afternoons were spent at the local movie theater, where, for twenty-five cents, you could spend the whole afternoon watching all the high-riding heroes. Back then, twenty-five cents bought a movie ticket, a soda pop, a candy bar, an ice cream and some popcorn. If we were lucky enough to find plenty of soda pop bottles to cash in, we'd have enough money left over to buy a few comic books.

Being born and raised in a rural environment I was no stranger to livestock—especially horses, which I went to any length to be around. I worked for nothing at local riding stables and horse auctions just for the opportunity to ride. As I got older, I ventured out and found that there were several dude ranches and weekend rodeos around the Northeast. My pals and I had a great time impressing the girls with our cowboy skills, or at least we thought we were impressing them. I had a little advantage over the others because I was the only one who could play and sing. Little did we know that wrangling dudes was a real cowboy's worst nightmare—next to maybe milking cows—but it sure beat the paper route and mowing lawns.

Looking back, I didn't do any more or any less than any other kid my age. I continued to make the little weekend rodeos and played music for just about anyone who would listen. Summer's end was always a drag thinking about going back to school. I hated the thought of classrooms and homework, but there was a bright side to all this: fall meant that October wasn't far off and the rodeo would be making its annual appearance at Boston Garden. Oh, they were two great weeks, and I spent every possible moment there. The wonderful memories linger with me of getting to see and meet Gene Autry, Roy Rogers, The Sons of the Pioneers and the Cass County Boys. I could go on and on. I'll never forget the nights in the Manger Hotel coffee shop meeting and visiting with Karl and Hugh Farr and Ray Whitley. I'll always remember how intently I listened to their stories and talked with them until the wee hours of the morning. They were sure nice to me and never showed a lack of interest to my seemingly endless barrage of questions. Somehow they must have known my sincere interest and love of western music.

Unlike most of the kids I hung around with, I knew the difference between the real cowboys and the movie ones. There were some exceptions, like Tom Mix and Ken Maynard, who were real cowboys who happened to become movie stars. The same was true of another of my heroes, Casey Tibbs. He was a sure 'nuff cowboy, as were most rodeo cowboys of his era. I met Casey for the first time in Boston, and I'll always remember how kind and generous he was with his time for us wannabe cowboys. Some thirty years later, I became pretty good friends with him. The world lost a great cowboy the day Casey Tibbs rode over the Great Divide. Real legends and role models are as scarce as an honest politician in today's society. They just don't make 'em like they used to.

Every year when the rodeo pulled out of town, a little piece of me went with it until I couldn't stand the thought of being left behind. I felt like some kind of alien in my surroundings and I had to do something about it. I know it broke my mother's heart when I quit school in my eleventh

year. My dad wasn't all too happy either, but somehow he understood my adventuresome spirit, as he had done the same thing when he was a boy. I threw my suitcase and guitar into my 1951 Ford convertible and headed west. My destination was Texas—Dublin to be exact. I was going to the Lightning C Ranch in hopes of getting a job. I had gotten to know a few of the cowboys who worked for Everett Colborn when they came to Boston every year. I thought this would be a good place to start.

Well, as luck would have it, this maiden voyage was to be short-lived. I began having trouble with my car just outside New York—not the best place to have car trouble. I repaired what I thought to be the problem but decided to make a little detour to my old hometown, where one of my cousins had a garage. About twenty miles from Boonton, the engine threw a rod, and that was the end of that. Having to hang around for a week while my cousin rebuilt the engine put a strain on my

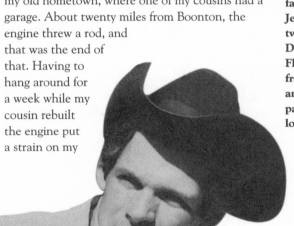

Young Don pauses for a moment at the old family home in New Jersey (above). At twenty-something, Don worked at Six Flags Over Texas from 1960 to 1964 and helped build the park's first steam locomotive (below).

Uncle Ned checks out Don's new Red Ryder BB rifle at Christmastime 1948 (above). Don poses with his guns, which he used as a "gunfighter and cowboy singer" at Six Flags Over Texas (right).

cash, so I had no choice but to stay and work for a while. I went to work playing in some godforsaken beer joint in Dover, New Jersey. It was your typical bucket-of-blood-chicken-wire-'round-the-whole-place kind of gig. This is where I learned my first lesson in survival and self-preservation: when a fight breaks out, keep on playing. If you're the intended target, protect your body and your instrument by getting the hell out of there. Only in the case of a life-threatening situation do you use your instrument as a weapon. I've since played in hundreds of bars and clubs and only gotten involved in a fight once. Not bad when you consider how many "Hey, Tex, where's your horse?" remarks I tolerated.

That was all part of paying your dues. I don't regret a day of it. I believe there's a reason for everything, and Texas just wasn't part of the plan at the time. Had I ignored my gut feelings and gone on to Texas, I might never have met Elton Britt, with whom I toured the clubs and military bases of the Northeast for a while. I might never have gotten the opportunity to open shows for Ray Price, Hank Thompson, Carl Smith and Johnny Cash. I might never have met Herb Hooven, who became my close friend and mentor. Herb taught me how to take constructive criticism and is one of the most brilliant musicians I have ever known.

One of the most important things I learned in those early years was that there are only two kinds of music: good and bad. I believe that was a quote from Miles Davis, but regardless, it still means that no matter what type of music you choose, if it's good, play it; if it's bad, don't. Play for the love of it and not for the money. People can tell the difference.

It's quite obvious that cowboy and western music are my favorite, but I also love all kinds of traditional music, from old-time country (when country meant country) to early jazz, to folk blues and western swing. These varied influences were challenging and mind-developing. Why, I was always wanting to know who influenced whom, who wrote this or that song, where some old song came from. I became a self-taught historian of sorts. I'm still doing all that, except now they call me a musicologist. All this has probably done me more harm than good as far as "making it" in the music business. But fame and fortune have never been very high on my list of accomplishments. It has always bothered me that everything had to be in some sort of category and judged solely on its monetary value.

These are probably some of the reasons I was so heavily influenced by Marty Robbins. His roots were deep in the western tradition, yet he recorded everything from country to pop to Hawaiian to Mexican ballads. The same held true for Jimmie Rodgers and Gene Autry. No one in recent times, with the exception of Willie Nelson and Merle Haggard, has successfully been able to pull that off.

Those good gigs with singers I idolized were few and far between. It was mostly roadhouses by night and unloading freight cars by day. Texas was still hard on my mind, and I was bound and determined I wasn't going to spend one more miserable winter in that cold north country. I traded the car for a 1941 Ford pickup, which I made into a crude sort of camper, and headed west. I arrived in Fort Worth in the fall of 1959.

Jobs weren't all that plentiful, especially playing jobs, but I was never too proud to do whatever I had to do to make a living. I did find out, though, that there was one exception: I couldn't work at a regular indoor job. I couldn't stand being shut up in some building for eight hours. I had taken this assembly-line-factory job thinking I could tough it out for a while, but I only lasted until noon the first day. I went to lunch and never went back.

A few days later I was reading the want ads in the newspaper and ran across an advertisement for a new theme park that was opening, called Six Flags Over Texas. The ad listed all kinds of jobs, but the only one that caught my eye was "Now holding auditions for gunfighters and cowboy singers." What a stroke of luck! I was camped out on their doorstep bright and early the next morning. I auditioned with "Cattle Call" and "The Strawberry Roan." They were most impressed with my yodeling. Then they asked me if I knew how to handle a gun and how many more of those cowboy songs did I know. I told them I knew a thousand of them old songs and I could shoot straighter than Tom Mix. I got the job, but singin' 'n' shootin' wasn't the first of my duties. I worked all winter at the park helping two old-time railroad men build the park's first steam locomotive.

A few weeks before the park opened, we went into rehearsals for the gunfighters shows. I never dreamed these shows would be so elaborate. True, they were somewhat tongue-in-cheek but very authentic. The shows were choreographed by top Hollywood stuntmen who taught us everything from elaborate falls to the proper use of various weapons. We had a hanging routine that was so realistic we had to take it out of the show the first week the park opened because it was scaring too many kids, and ladies were fainting.

We rotated four skits every twenty minutes, twelve hours a day, seven days a week. It was a grueling schedule for one hundred and fifty dollars a week, but we had a great time. The off seasons got pretty lean, so I took a job hauling oil-field supplies for Fort Worth Pipe and Supply Company out of Fort Worth. I traveled all over Texas, Oklahoma, Kansas, Nebraska and parts of New Mexico.

When my first record came out in January 1964 ("The Young Ranger" on Ren Records of Dallas, Texas), I took a box or two with me in the truck and stopped in every town that had a radio station and gave them a copy of my record to play. I did the same at all the truck stops, asking if they'd put my record on their jukeboxes. That record did pretty good on a regional basis. This was in the

days when a disc jockey could play whatever he or she felt like playing if they thought it was good enough to warrant air play. These radio personalities, as they were known in those days, were well known and liked in their communities. Many were known nationally, but all of them knew the music and the artists, unlike today's dictator-ruled button pushers who can only play what they are told to play. On the other hand, I can happily admit there are still many great radio personalities out there, many of them friends of mine, whose knowledge and expertise go far beyond the Top Forty.

I left Six Flags after the close of the 1964 season but continued to drive for Fort Worth Pipe for a short while after that. I played off and on at the Cowtown Jamboree at the Majestic Theater in Fort Worth, as well as at Panther Hall. Lots of good times and great music in that old place. My biggest thrill was opening for Tex Ritter there. Needless to say, he was a big hero of mine, and we hit it off pretty good when he heard me singing those cowboy songs. Of all the singing cowboys, Tex was the one who stuck closest to the traditional roots. He knew a million of those old cowboy songs and where every one of them came from, as well.

In spite of the minor triumphs and setbacks during those years, I was getting pretty restless and anxious for my career to take hold a little quicker than it was. The peaks and valleys in the entertainment world are both higher and lower than in any other business. Some days I was higher than Mt. McKinley, and others I was lower than Death Valley. Too much of this can become dangerous to your health, as well as to everyone around you. I had to make a move, but I also had a wife and two small children to support. My wife at that time wasn't very supportive of my show business career. She was always telling me to get a real job and forget all this guitar-playing foolishness. Then one day, out of pure desperation, I told her I was going to Nashville. I said if I didn't get anything going, I'd come back, quit playing music and get a "real" job.

Why I went there I'll never know. I guess because it was the center of country music. But I had a feeling I was too eclectic for their tastes. That was confirmed a few days later when I met with Pete Drake of Stop Records. He listened to my little reel-to-reel demo, then looked at me and said, "You should have gone to Greenwich Village instead of coming here." I thought at first he was just trying to be funny, but looking back, strange as

St. Patrick's gravesite outside of Belfast, Ireland, is the scene of this gathering, which includes a local officer and his dog, Paul McCallum, Don Edwards, Bo Jimison, Steve Murrin, an unidentified piper, a local government official, and an executive from British Caledonian Airways, the sponsor of the tour (above). Young daughters Dayle and Llayne dance to the music that their father is composing (below right).

it may seem, he was absolutely right. I did wind up recording two records for Stop, but they didn't do much.

Just about the time I was giving serious thought to packing it in, I met this promoter who was putting together a Canadian club tour. It sounded too good to be true—and it was. He put together a five-piece band and hired a road manager for the tour. We were to start somewhere around Toronto and work our way to British Columbia. We would be playing six nights a week and traveling on the seventh. The only problem was how we were going to get there. Well, Woody the road manager said he had a bus and everything would be fine. In reality, he was just road testing this bus and told the owner he would have it back after a weekend gig. He forgot to tell the guy the gig was in Canada.

The bus was an old 1946 Flexible and didn't look like it would make it out of town. On the day we were leaving, I called my wife and told her the good news that I got a job and would send home the money as soon as we got paid. She was less than excited about me going on a month-long tour. I really couldn't blame her.

I don't remember how much money we were supposed to get paid. It was bad enough having to pay six people, but Woody went and hired a girl singer. He had her dressed up like an Indian and called her Little Mohea, or something like that. I think she was part Indian and she could sing good, but we still had to pay her. We looked like a Bronco Billy troupe going down the road.

Much to my surprise, things went along pretty good the first couple of weeks—at least as far as I can remember they did. I do remember all the venues were owned by Chinese and were all a restaurant-and-club-type combination. I remember this place in Saskatchewan. I know it was pretty far up there because the road only went south, east and west. The only road going north was dog sled tracks. Our meals came with the gig, so we didn't go hungry—that is, if you like Chinese food, which luckily I did. The place was packed that night, mostly Eskimos and Indians having a great time. Somebody requested I sing "Kawliga." Thinking nothing of it, I went right into the song and everybody started dancing, having a hell of a time. When all of a sudden here comes the club owner waving his arms and yelling "Stop! . . . Stop! . . . Stop! . . . He was waving a big butcher knife at the band, still yelling, "No pray that song, No pray that song!" I got him quieted down long enough to find out that whenever a band would play "Kawliga," a big fight always broke out. Well, we went back to playing and everything went along real fine until we started playing "Cotton Eyed Joe." I'll be damned but if here he didn't come again. He runs right up to the bandstand and starts in to waving that butcher knife at the band pointing at each band member, yelling, "You fiah, you fiah, you fiah," and so forth until he came to me. Again I calmed him down long enough to explain that he couldn't fire each individual band member; he had to fire the whole band or nothing.

We finished out the week there without further incident and headed west for Alberta. We arrived at the club on Monday afternoon and were greeted by the owner, who said he was glad to see us and bought us all a drink before dinner. We played that night to a pretty good house for a Monday night. When we finished playing, the owner called our road manager into his office and said this would be our last night. When the band and I heard about this, we wanted to know why we were being fired. As I recall, he didn't give much of an excuse, which made Woody mad. Woody reminded him we had a contract, and he immediately told us what we could do with it. This made us all the madder, and just as we were going to grab that little weasel, the bouncer walked up between Woody and me and stuck a pistol in Woody's ribs and told us in no uncertain terms that we were leaving. I told Woody not to argue with them anymore and just take the one night's pay and get the hell out of there. It sure wasn't worth getting killed for—and

besides, they were holding all the cards. Why, there's no telling what could have happened to us up in that remote region of northern Alberta.

The next morning we all unanimously voted to return to the U.S. We headed straight south and kept going south until we didn't see any more snow. About four days later and nearly broke, we arrived in Las Vegas, Nevada. We never did find a gig, but it sure felt good to get warm after three weeks of snow up to our ears and freezing our butts off. Woody called the agent in Nashville to see if he could line us up with something on the way back, but to no avail. We did find out why we got run off from that club after only one night of a six-night stand, though. They had used us to cover for a band that got stranded in British Columbia. The old "double booking" scam. This was just one of those gigs from hell that was doomed from the start.

I have since been back to Canada on several occasions and had a great time. I've got a lot of fans and friends up there, and all that misfortune could have happened anywhere—and has since.

I have a difficult and often painful time bridging the years between the late 1960s and the mid-1970s. They were years of uncertainty that were causing heartache and unhappiness to my family and people around me. I was working so hard at such unrealistic goals

Don sits astride his horse, Rebel, on the West Fork Ranch near Fort Worth, Texas.

A great deal of
Don's time is
spent traveling by
pickup from one
performance to
another.

that all I had left to show for my selfish quest for success was a cheap guitar and a failed marriage. My life was pretty aimless after the divorce, and I'm mighty brain cloudy concerning my whereabouts during that time. Once again I was back to hard scrabbling, drifting from one job to another until I was summoned back to Massachusetts upon receiving news of my father's untimely death at the age of sixty-two. If that wasn't bad enough, three years later my youngest daughter, Dayle, was killed by a car in California. These were the most heartbreaking and bleakest years of my life. I no longer had the happy-go-lucky, devil-may-care spirit of previous years. I was never what one would consider an outgoing person and seldom showed any outward emotion; still, I became more withdrawn and introverted than ever. The only way I knew to come to grips with all this tragedy was to go back to Texas and start over.

A few days later, I said my good-byes and headed west. I hadn't got forty miles down the road when I was pulled over by the police. I thought they were going to give me a speeding ticket, but instead they told me to get out of the car. They slapped handcuffs on me and put me into the back seat of their police car. I kept asking them what the hell was going on, but they never would give me a straight answer, other than they were taking me downtown to ask a few questions. When we got to the police station, they charged me with car theft, fingerprinted me, emptied my pockets and locked me in a cell like I was a bank robber or something. It may sound hard to believe, but I was locked up in that cell for nearly thirty-six hours. Finally, this detective comes and takes me into a room and asks me a bunch of questions. About an hour later, he tells me I'm free to go and made

some half-hearted apology about me being the wrong man. My car had matched the description of a stolen car that was used in a robbery and just happened to have Texas license plates that were one digit different from mine.

The rest of my trip was uneventful, even pleasant at times. I had a lot of time to be by myself and think. I love driving and thinking. I felt a peacefulness I hadn't felt for a long time. As I crossed the New Jersey line, I got to thinking about the old home place and wondered how much had changed in the nearly thirty years since I had moved away. I decided to take a little detour. What would it hurt to check out old Boonton one more time?

> *I think I'll take me back again*
> *   to see my old hometown.*
> *I don't expect to find her*
> *   still a bride in wedding gown,*
> *But only that she still recall*
> *   the one who loved her so*
> *And lead me down the old familiar streets*
> *   we used to know.*
> —"OLD HOME TOWN," BOB NOLAN

I turned off Highway 46 and drove out to the old home place. The house was still there, but the road was paved and the farms were gone. It sure wasn't too rural anymore, but not as bad as I thought it would be. I drove out past Uncle Wally's place and over to Uncle Ernie's—not a familiar face anywhere. I drove on up the hill to the Grange hall where they used to hold the Saturday night dances. I don't remember much about the old place, but I can still hear the music.

I felt kind of sad as I drove toward town looking for maybe just one familiar face among all those strangers, but knowing that all my relatives had long since moved on. I drove out past the railroad station. I can still see me standing on the platform holding my dad's hand as the train slowly rolled into the station pulled by one of the last of the great steam locomotives. I remember all that belching steam and those huge driving wheels.

Saturday memories came back as I parked near the old State Theater where I saw my first cowboy movie. It's a video store now—what a horrible thought. I remember the old cafe next door where I had breakfast on Saturday mornings with my dad and uncles. We'd all eat and the men would talk a while, then they'd go off to buy supplies and stuff, leaving me at the picture show for the day.

I had something to eat and, as I recall, it wasn't much better than the processed fodder you find in any fast-food joint. As I paid my bill, I got to thinking that it's wonderful to have memories, because you can't come back. They were good days then, but now they're far away. Even the coffee was cold at the Come Home Cafe.

> *There's a strangeness in the air today.*
>   *Have I come home or have I lost my way?*
> *This just can't be the old hometown*
>   *I gave my dreams to hold,*
> *There's too much makeup on her face,*
>   *Her eyes are much too cold.*
> "OLD HOME TOWN," BOB NOLAN

As I drove out of town I knew I wouldn't be back this way again, or at least not in the foreseeable future. It was getting on toward that time of the evening when the soft light of sundown brings on that nostalgic melancholy, but I couldn't let myself dwell on it like I sometimes do. I had a long way to go and it wasn't the time to be looking back.

I headed on south through Maryland and Virginia, turning west through Tennessee. I never even slowed down going through Nashville. I'd enough of that town to last me a lifetime. Now don't get me wrong, Nashville is a beautiful city with warm friendly people. There are some of the finest and most brilliant musicians and songwriters

in the world there. It was the "business" of music that I disliked. Music factories belching out overproduced, homogenized pablum for the unsuspecting masses. There's a world of difference between manufacturing music for money and creating art for love, but I also thought that having talent mattered. Oh well, there's more important things on my mind right now. I can go without eating for the next couple of days, I hope I've got enough gas money to get me to Texas.

I made it to Fort Worth all right side up with care and managed to find a few playing jobs over the next several months. It wasn't long until I met Joe Dulle, owner of the White Elephant Saloon in the Fort Worth Stockyards. It seems ironic that here I was, back in familiar surroundings playing the music that started my career some fifteen years before. It's even more ironic that I was playing in the same place where, in 1908, John Lomax collected many of his cowboy songs. If I never believed in destiny, I do now. How else to explain why I wound up here. Why the White Elephant Saloon? Why the Fort Worth Stockyards? How does one explain the mystic trails of life? It's not just the trail itself or where it leads to. It has to do with how hard it is to travel. Now, none of life's trails are free from obstacles and switchbacks; it's just that the ones less traveled are more challenging and rewarding.

Kathy and Don pause from a rigorous schedule to enjoy each other's company (above). At the Long X Ranch in Kent, Texas, Don relaxes with his favorite guitar (below).

Two roads diverged in a yellow wood,
And sorry I could not travel both
And be one traveler, long I stood
And looked down one as far as I could
To where it bent in the undergrowth;

Then took the other, as just as fair,
And having perhaps the better claim,
Because it was grassy and wanted wear;
Though as for that the passing there
Had worn them really about the same,

And both that morning equally lay
In leaves no step had trodden black.
Oh, I kept the first for another day!
Yet knowing how way leads into way,
I doubted if I should ever come back.

I shall be telling this with a sigh
Somewhere ages and ages hence:
Two roads diverged in a wood, and I—
I took the one less traveled by,
And that has made all the difference.
—ROBERT FROST

"Top hand and ranch boss," Kathy stops for a moment before going about her daily chores.

It did make a difference—a big difference. I could fill another book just on my fourteen years or so in the stockyards. It seems there was hardly a night went by that didn't turn into a memorable occasion. Like the impromptu jam sessions with Roy Clark, James Galway and William Walker of the Metropolitan Opera. I got to know hundreds of people who would become dedicated fans, some of whom became close and cherished personal friends. But nothing can compare to the night I met Kathy Jean Davis. She was the most beautiful and stunning woman I had ever laid eyes on. She became my lover, partner, my best friend and the joy of my life. We were married on January 7, 1978, and have so far shared sixteen wonderful years together.

I left the White Elephant in 1986 so I could devote more time to touring, writing and recording. I wanted more time for study and research projects. I still continue to make three or four appearances a year at the White Elephant; after all, it was and is a major part of my life. But I began to miss my cowboy friends. I missed those rare but wonderful opportunities going out with the wagon in the spring, being a-horseback, and the feeling you get knowing you did an honest day's work.

I wasn't born into ranching or cowboydom, either one. It was an intentional effort on my part to at least experience the lifestyle firsthand. I have, and still do partake in cowboying in one capacity or another, but I don't claim to be no cowboy. I'll leave that distinction to those a-horseback who draw their wages punching cows.

Regrettably, as I look back, I never became a full-time participant in the cowboy life. I was only passing through. A wide-eyed, adventuresome kid with a war bag of dreams and a wore-out guitar.

For the last forty years or so, I have been fortunate to have known, lived among, and to have as friends cowboys and cowpeople to whom I owe a debt of gratitude for shaping my life with their teachings and friendship, which to this day I cherish above all else.

At the National Cowboy Hall of Fame in Oklahoma City, Don receives the Western Heritage Wrangler Award for Best Traditional Western Music for 1991 (above). "It ain't all ridin' and singin'," says Don, as he rolls out wire for fencing on his Sevenshoux Ranch in Weatherford, Texas (left).

Abilene

The great Amon Carter of Fort Worth, Texas, had a saying: "Fort Worth is where the West begins, and Dallas is where the East peters out." This is true in more ways than one. There is a definite topographical and geographical change when you are coming west out of Dallas. The two cities are worlds apart in culture and attitude, as well.

Geographically, Dallas is located in Texas, but with its eastern big-city mentality, it could just as well be New York or Chicago. Fort Worth has remained a cow town, but with modern conveniences.

Fort Worth is still where the West begins, but Abilene is where the West still is. It has an Old West flavor, and the people are friendly if you're friendly to them: no airs, no questions about where a man is from or where he's going.

This song is an old one. I have no idea who wrote the original, but it's deep in the folk blues idiom. It has been rewritten many times and made popular over the years by many singers, from Bob Gibson to George Hamilton IV. I believe this version is one of the earliest known.

ABILENE

Traditional
Arrangement and Adaptation by Don Edwards

Abilene, Abilene,
Prettiest town I ever seen;
Folks out there don't treat you mean
In Abilene, my Abilene.

I sit alone most every night
Watching the trains as they pull out of sight.
Don't I wish they would carry me back
To Abilene, my Abilene.

Been to Chicago, Frisco, too;
Detroit city just won't do.
Lord, how I wish that I could be
Back in Abilene, my Abilene.

Saw New York City in the drizzling rain,
Headlights flickering on my window pane.
Made me so lonesome for
My Abilene, old Abilene.

Old empty boxcars standing all alone,
Wheels all rusted—it ain't no home.
How I wish they could carry me back
To Abilene, my Abilene.

Crowded city ain't nothing free;
Nothing in this town for me.
So I'll just be heading home
Back to Abilene, my Abilene.

G   B7

Ab - i - lene,   Ab - i - lene,

C   G   A7

Pret - ti - est town   I _____ ev - er seen;   Folks out there _____

D7   G   C7   G

__ don't treat you mean   In Ab - i - lene,   my Ab - i - lene.

Katherine Field .55.

Annie Laurie / Bad Half Hour

This wonderful Charles "Badger" Clark poem has been set to music many times. I put some music to it back in 1985, but I always thought it was too fast for the night-herding mood of the actual poem.

A couple of years ago I was playing a Scottish festival in Texas where I met Alex Beaton, a Scottish folksinger, and Alasdair Fraser, one of Scotland's finest and foremost fiddle players. We sang and played together that day, and it was one of the most memorable musical times of my life. We played "Annie Laurie," a well-known folk song from that country. Alex sang it like it's never been sung before, and Alasdair played one of the most beautiful and moving fiddle breaks I'd ever heard. Then Alex said, "Why don't you sing that cowboy song to the tune of 'Annie Laurie'?" Well, Badger's poem came to life like never before—a magical musical moment, to say the least—and I've been singing it like that ever since.

I play this song in the key of A with a capo on the second fret in G position.

ANNIE LAURIE

Traditional

Max Welton's braes are bonnie where early falls the dew,
And 'twas there that Annie Laurie gave me her promise true;
Gave me her promise true, and ne'er forget will I,
And for bonnie Annie Laurie, I'd lay me down and die.

BAD HALF HOUR

Charles "Badger" Clark
Arrangement and Adaptation by Don Edwards

Wonder why I feel so restless—
Moon is shinin' still and bright,
Cattle all is restin' easy—
But I just can't sleep tonight.
Ain't no cactus in my blankets;
Don't know why they feel so hard,
'Less it's Warblin' Jim a-singin'
"Annie Laurie" out on guard.

"Annie Laurie," wish he'd quit it!
Couldn't sleep now if I tried.
Makes the night seem big and lonesome
And my throat feel sore inside.
How my Annie used to sing it,
And it sounded good and gay;
Nights I drove her home from dances
When the East was turnin' gray.

Yes, "her brow was like the snowdrift"
And her eyes like quiet streams,
"And her face" I still can see it
Much too frequent in my dreams;
And her hand was soft and trembly
That night underneath the tree,
When I couldn't help but tell her
She was "all the world to me."

But her folks said I was "shif'less,"
"Wild," "unsettled"—they was right,
For I leaned to punchin' cattle,
And I'm at it still tonight.
And she married young Doc Wilkins.
Oh my Lord! but that was hard!
Wish that fool would quit his singin'
"Annie Laurie" out on guard!

Oh, I just can't stand it thinkin'
Of the things that happened then.
Good old times, and all apast me!
Never seem to come again.
My turn? Sure. I'll come a-runnin';
Warm me up some coffee, pard.
But I'll stop that Jim from singin'
"Annie Laurie" out on guard.

Max Wel-ton's braes are bon-nie where ear-ly falls the dew, And 'twas there that An-nie Lau-rie gave me her prom-ise true; Gave me her prom-ise true, and ne'er for-get will I, And for bon-nie An-nie Lau-rie, I'd lay me down and die.

The Ballad Hunter

This was the opening song for my little book and tape anthology, *Songs of the Cowboy.* The song and the project was my tribute to Nathan Howard "Jack" Thorp, the pioneer collector of cowboy songs.

For those of you not familiar with Jack Thorp, I strongly suggest you read his biography, *Pardner of the Wind,* especially chapter one: "Banjo in the Cow Camps." I have read this chapter so many times I can almost recite it. The whole book, in fact, has been as much an inspiration as Will James's *Lone Cowboy.*

It also goes without saying that you need to find a copy of Thorp's *Songs of the Cowboys,* first published in 1908 and again in 1921 as a larger version. Jack was the first to publish a book of cowboy songs, two years prior to John Lomax's monumental collection in 1910. Mr. Lomax deserves all the credit he has received, but I more closely relate to Thorp, a true singing cowboy and a sure 'nough cowpuncher.

The melody here is pretty much like "Little Joe, the Wrangler," for obvious reasons.

THE BALLAD HUNTER

Don Edwards

Long ago, there was a man who rode throughout the West
Collecting songs and poetry and verses of the range.
He wrote "Little Joe, the Wrangler" and "The Pecos River Queen";
A ballad-huntin' cowboy, and Jack Thorp was his name.

Jack was a big man and friendly sort o' guy;
He had a way with horses, played a banjo-mandolin—
A sure 'nough cowpuncher from his boots to his wide-brimmed hat,
A singin' buckaroo, and a pardner of the wind.

One night while trailin' horses, Jack rode up to camp.
On the night air, a cowboy song came driftin' soft and low,
A song he never heard before 'bout a steel dust cuttin' horse,
The fastest one in Texas, by the name of Dodgin' Joe.

The banjo-playin' cowboy knew two verses of the song;
He sang 'em once again while Jack wrote down the words.
How many songs were written yet never written down?
Jack knew there must be plenty more out there he hadn't heard.

Next mornin' he had breakfast, wrote a letter to his boss:
"I've made up my mind to keep driftin' on my own.
I've quit huntin' horses, started huntin' cowboy songs.
When you see my dust arrivin', I'll be comin' home."

A cowboy song is just like gold; it's anywhere it's found—
From a cow camp down in Texas to a saloon in Idaho.
So with old Gray Dog, his saddle horse, and his packhorse, Ample, too,
They traveled down those ballad trails in search of Dodgin' Joe.

Jack became the first to collect the cowboy songs—
Songs about the hard life and the free life on the range.
A living part of cowboy life was saved because of him,
And now I find the time has come for me to do the same.

Those songs are harder now to find than they were long ago.
Most folks think I'm crazy; they say the cowboy life is gone.
But their greed and city ways haven't killed us off as yet,
So as long as there are cowboys, there'll be a cowboy song.

'Cause a cowboy song is still like gold; it's anywhere it's found—
From a cow camp down in Texas, to a saloon in Idaho.
With my trusty pet horse, Rebel, and my packhorse, Pecos, too,
We'll travel down those ballad trails like Jack did long ago.

Long a-go, there was a man who rode through-out the West Col-

lect-ing songs and po-e-try and vers-es of the range. He wrote

"Lit-tle Joe, the Wrang-ler" and "The Pe-cos Riv-er Queen"; A

bal-lad hunt-in' cow-boy, and Jack Thorp was his name.

The Brazos

This is one of the oldest songs in Texas. It names most all the rivers south of the Canadian. There is a longer version called "The Rivers of Texas," but most people aren't familiar with it. Most Texas folksingers know this song, and its chorus is great for a sing-a-long.

I recorded "The Brazos" on my first album for Warner/Western called *Songs of the Trail*. I sing it a little differently in person than on the recording, because Nashville can't stand anything that might go over three minutes. I don't know why they worry so much because all the world's great music will never be heard on the radio—at least, not anytime soon.

Fear not, my friends, this music is here for you to sing and play forever.

THE BRAZOS

Traditional

We crossed the wide Pecos, we forded the Nueces,
We swum the Guadalupe, we followed the Brazos.
Red River runs rusty, the Wichita clear,
But it was down by the Brazos, I courted my dear.

Chorus:
Li-le-li-lee, give me your hand, (3x)
There's many a river that waters the land.

The fair Angelina runs glossy and gliding,
The crooked Colorado runs weaving and winding,
The slow Antonio courses the plain,
But I never will walk by the Brazos again.

Chorus:
Li-le-li-lee, pull the boat on, (3x)
My Brazos River sweetheart has left me and gone.

She kissed me, she hugged me, she called me her dandy.
The Trinity is muddy, the Brazos quicksandy;
She kissed me, she hugged me, she called me her own,
But down by the Brazos, she left me alone.

Chorus:
Li-le-li-lee, give me your hand, (3x)
The Trinity is muddy, the Brazos quicksand.

The girls of Little River, they're sweet and they're pretty,
The Sabine and the Sober have many a beauty,
By the banks of Nacogdoches, there's girls by the score,
But down by the Brazos, I'll wander no more.

Chorus:
Li-le-li-lee, give me your hand, (3x)
There's many a river that waters the land.

We crossed the wide Pe - cos, we ford - ed the Nu - e - ces, we swum the Guad - a -

lu - pe, we fol - lowed the Braz - os. Red Riv - er runs rust - y, the Wich - i - ta

clear, But it was down by the Braz - os, I court - ed my dear. Li - le - li -

Chorus

lee, give me your hand Li - le - li - lee, give me your hand

Li - le - li - lee, give me your hand, There's man - y a riv - er that

wa - ters the land. There's man - y a riv - er that wa - ters the land.

Bronco Peelers Song

I took poetic license to rewrite this song a little bit and put a tune of my own to it. Sounds bad sometimes, but isn't this the way we keep these old songs from passing into obscurity? It's a part of the folk process.

Jack Thorp made reference to this song in his second edition of *Songs of the Cowboys*. He said he didn't know who wrote it, but he'd first heard it sung by L. Brennon at Indian Tanks, New Mexico.

BRONCO PEELERS SONG

Traditional
Music by Don Edwards

I've been upon the prairie; I've been upon the plain;
Drove cattle on the Goodnight Trail and slept out in the rain;
I've rode through blinding hailstorms, all kinds of wind and snow.
I'll tell you, boys, I hate to see the good times come and go.

Chorus:
Good-bye, Liza; good-bye, Liza Jane;
Good-bye, little Liza; she died out on the plain.

I hate to see the wire fence a-closin' up the range
And all this filling in the trail with people who are strange.
We boys don't know how to plow nor reap the golden grain,
But to round up steers and brand the cows, to us was always plain.

Chorus

I've roped wild cattle flying through the brush;
I've rode the streets of hell, boys, in a mighty damn big rush;
I've rode across the desert in boxcars on the rail;
I can ride a pitching pony till the hair comes off his tail.

Chorus

So when this blasted country is all closed in with the wire,
And all the top with crabgrass is burning in Sol's fire,
I hope them settlers will be glad when the rain hits the land,
And all us cowdogs are in hell burning the devil's brand.

Chorus

I've been up-on ___ the prai-rie; I've been up-on the plain; ___ Drove

cat-tle on ___ the Good-night Trail and slept out in the rain; ___ I've

rode through blind — ing hail-storms, all kinds of wind and snow. ___ I'll

Chorus

tell you, boys, I hate to see ___ the good times come and go. Good-bye, ___ Li — za;

good-bye, Li — za Jane; ___ Good-bye, lit-tle Li — za; she died out on the plain. ___

The Campfire Has Gone Out

Jack Thorp included this song in his second and larger publication of *Songs of the Cowboys.* He said he had first heard it sung in the San Andreas Mountains and seemed to think it was written by Eugene Manlove Rhodes, who never admitted to its authorship. Like so many old songs, they've been passed around so often that their author or authors have been forgotten or passed into history without due credit. It is possible it might have been written by Ben Arnold Connor, an old-time frontiersman and cowboy. He took credit for it in his autobiography, *Rekindling Campfires,* edited by North Dakota historian Lewis F. Crawford.

I have taken the liberty to set this to my own music and change a few words here and there to make it into sort of a cowboy protest song.

THE CAMPFIRE HAS GONE OUT

Music by Don Edwards
Based on a poem possibly written by Ben Arnold Connor or
Eugene Manlove Rhodes

Through the progress of our country, our occupation's gone;
So we put our ideas into words and our words into a song.
Somewhere 'tween the wire and the comin' of the train,
We let it slip away and wonder who's to blame.

Bid 'em all adieu, you can't turn the world about.
The cowboy left the country, and the campfire has gone out.

When I think of those good old days, my eyes with tears do fill.
I think of the tin can by the fire and the coyote on the hill;
I think of riding night guard while the stars were shining bright;
But now instead the wire fence guards the herd tonight.

You'll miss him on the roundup, it's gone his merry shout.
The cowboy left the country, and the campfire has gone out.

I'll tell you, boys, in them days old-timers stood a show;
Never had much money, not a sorrow did we know.
But, oh, how things have changed, now we're poorly clothed and fed;
Our wagons are all broken, and our ponies most all dead.

Bid 'em all adieu, we can hear the angels shout;
"Oh, here they come to heaven; the campfire has gone out."

The cowboy, like the Red Man, you had to leave your land;
Can't raise your stock and plant your crop in the gumbo and the sand.
Greed disguised as progress has put us to the test
They won't be glad until we're gone from our home out in the West.

It's sad to see those good old days replaced with greed and doubt;
Soon we'll leave the country, the campfire has gone out.

Bid 'em all adieu, you can't turn the world about;
Oh, here we come to heaven; the campfire has gone out.

E   **A**   **E**

Through the prog-ress of our coun-try, our oc-cu-pa-tion's gone; So we

F#   **B7**

put our i-deas in-to words and our words in-to a song.

E   **A**   **E**

Some-where 'tween the wire and the com-in' of the train, We

B7   **E**

let it slip a-way, and we won-der who's _ to blame.

A   **E**   **A**   **E**

Bid 'em all a-dieu, _ you can't turn the world a-bout. The

B7   **E**

cow-boy left the coun-try, and the camp-fire has gone out. _____

Chant of the Night Songs

I wrote this song in 1986. It first appeared in my book and tape anthology *Songs of the Cowboy*. I have since changed the words and the melody a little.

Night-herding ballads have always been a favorite of mine—songs like "The Night Herding Song" by Harry Stephens, Badger Clark's "Bad Half Hour"/"Annie Laurie," and Mike Burton's "Night Rider's Lament."

Night herding, or night guard as it was called, was one of the most important and loneliest jobs that the cowboy had. It consisted generally of two men working two-hour shifts. They would ride slowly around the herd in opposite directions meeting at intervals, thus letting each other know of their positions and that all was okay. It was at night when the cattle were most restless and likely to stampede that the cowboy's singing was a necessity. He would hum, whistle, or sing some old tune he knew. This singing had a soothing effect, preventing any sudden noise from startling the cattle. Mostly, the singing was to entertain themselves, something to do to stay awake during an uneventful night-guard shift, which was more likely than most stories lead you to believe.

For a really great night-herding story, read "Night Herd" in Charley Russell's *Trails Plowed Under*.

CHANT OF THE NIGHT SONGS

Don Edwards

When day's work is over and suppertime's gone,
I'll tell you the story of the night rider's song—
That long lonesome whistle and tunes with no words—
The Chant of the Night Songs we sang 'round the herd.

Cattle on the bed ground I hope that they'll stay
Till we're back on the trail at the breaking of day.
But until dawn I hope that they'll sleep;
Rest easy, weary cattle, to the cowboy's melody.

My trusty little night horse, he's gentle and smart;
He's heard my songs so much, he knows 'em by heart—
The creak of the saddle, a loose bridle rein,
His hoofs keeping time to "Poor Liza Jane."

Got to keep the herd settled; I don't want no stampede.
Two thousand running steers is what I don't need,
'Cause lightning and longhorns ain't no kind of game;
It's sure hell-for-leather through thunder and rain.

What keeps the herd from running, stampeding far and wide?
The range rider's moan and the Texas lullaby
In all kinds of weather, the lonely night through,
The Chant of the Night Songs—the night rider's blues.

Now the days of the range-riding cowboy are gone,
And the lonely night rider has sung his last song—
That long lonesome whistle and tunes with no words:
The Chant of the Night Songs, no more to be heard.

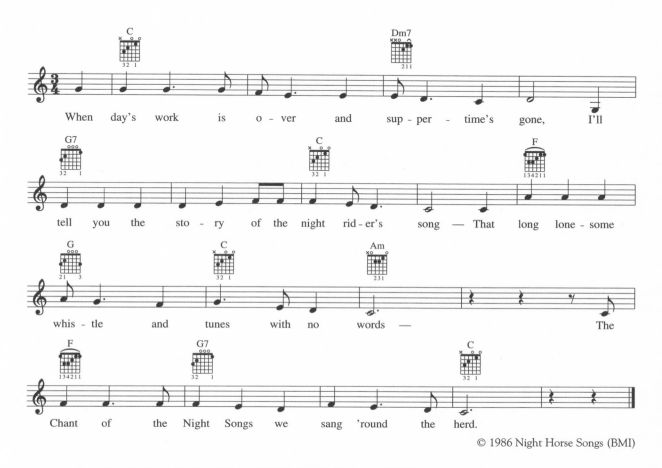

When day's work is o-ver and sup-per-time's gone, I'll tell you the sto-ry of the night rid-er's song — That long lone-some whis-tle and tunes with no words — The Chant of the Night Songs we sang 'round the herd.

Chopo

This is another of Jack Thorp's great songs. The only recording I have ever heard was by Buster Duncan of the Tune Wranglers from San Antonio, Texas. The Tune Wranglers were actual working cowboys who happened to be accomplished musicians as well. They were a popular cowboy string band during the late 1920s and into the '30s and '40s.

Chopo was one of Thorp's favorite horses, "the best night horse I ever had." He was a coal black offspring of a Morgan sire shipped from the East and out of a mustang Arabian mare from one of the old Spanish *caballadas* that ran all over the Southwest (*Pardner of the Wind,* pp. 51–53).

CHOPO

N. Howard "Jack" Thorp

Through rocky arroyos, so dark and so deep;
Down the sides of mountains, so slippery and steep;
You've good judgment, sure-footed, wherever you go;
You're a safety conveyance, my little Chopo.

Chorus:
Chopo, my pony; Chopo, my pride;
Chopo, mi amigo; Chopo I'll ride
From Mexico's border 'cross Texas Llanos;
To the salt Pecos River, I ride you, Chopo.

Whether single or double or in lead of a team,
Over highways or byways or crossing a stream,
You're always in fix and willing to go
Whenever you're called on, my chico Chopo.

Chorus

You're a good roping horse; you were never jerked down;
When tied to a steer, you will circle him 'round;
Let him once cross the string and over he'll go.
You sabe the business, my cow horse, Chopo.

Chorus

One day on the Llano, a hailstorm began;
The herds were stampeded, the horses all ran;
The lightning, it glittered; a cyclone did blow;
But you faced the sweet music, my little Chopo.

Chorus

The thunder and lightning for you had no fears;
You carried me safe with the stampedin' steers;
You're just a cow pony, but maybe you know
How much you are to me, my little Chopo.

Chorus

Through rock - y ar-roy - os, so dark and so deep; Down the sides of moun - tains, so

slip - pery and steep; You've good judg - ment, sure - foot-ed, wher-ev - er you go; __ You're a

safe - ty con-vey - ance, my lit - tle Chop - o. Chop - o, my po - ny;

Chop - o, my pride; Chop - o, mi a - mi - go; Chop - o I'll ride __ From

Mex - i - co's bor - der 'cross Tex - as Lla - nos; To the salt Pe - cos Riv - er, I ride you, Chop-o.

The Christmas Trail

This is another wonderful Badger Clark poem that I set to music. I only seem to sing it at Christmastime, but it ought to be sung all year long. The only recording of it is on Michael Martin Murphey's Christmas album *Cowboy Songs,* where Michael and I sang it as a duet.

THE CHRISTMAS TRAIL

Lyrics by Charles "Badger" Clark
Music by Don Edwards

The wind is blowin' cold down the mountain tips of snow,
And 'cross the ranges layin' brown and dead;
It's cryin' through the valley trees that wear the mistletoe
And mournin' with the gray clouds overhead.

Chorus:
Yet it's sweet with the beat of my little horse's feet,
And I whistle like the air was warm and blue,
For I'm ridin' up the Christmas trail to you, old folks;
I'm ridin' up the Christmas trail to you.

Oh, mebbe it was good when the whinny of the spring
Had wheeled me to hoppin' of the bars,
And livin' in the shadow of a sailin' buzzard's wing,
And sleepin' underneath a roof of stars.

Chorus:
But the bright campfire light only dances for a night,
While the home fire burns forever clear and true,
So 'round the year I circle back to you, old folks,
'Round the rovin' year I circle back to you.

Oh, mebbe it was good at the roundup in the fall
When the clouds of bawlin' dust before us ran,
And the pride of rope and saddle was a-drivin' of us all
To a stretch of nerve and muscle, man and man.

Chorus:
But the pride sort of died when the man got weary-eyed;
'Twas a sleepy boy that rode the night guard through,
And he dreamed himself along a trail to you, old folks,
Dreamed himself along a happy trail to you.

The coyote's winter howl cuts the dusk behind the hill,
But the ranch's shinin' window I can see,
And though I don't deserve it and, I reckon, never will,
There'll be room beside the fire kep' for me.

Chorus:
Skimp my plate 'cause I'm late. Let me hit the old kid gait,
For tonight I'm stumblin' tired of the new,
And I'm ridin' up the Christmas trail to you, old folks,
I'm ridin' up the Christmas trail to you.

Now the wind is blow-in' cold down the moun-tain tips of snow, And 'cross the rang-es ly-in' brown and

dead;   It's cry-in' through the val-ley trees that wear the mis-tle-toe   And

mourn-in' with the gray clouds o-ver-head.   Yet it's sweet with the beat of my

lit-tle hor-se's feet,   And I whis-tle like the air was warm and blue,   For I'm

rid-in' up the Christ-mas trail to you, old _ folks; I'm rid-in' up that Christ-mas trail to you.

Cowboy Jack

I don't remember when or where I first heard "Cowboy Jack." It appeared in Ira Sires's *Songs of the Open Range* in 1928 and has since been recorded many times. The song can also be found in my friend Jim Bob Tinsley's wonderful cowboy songbook, *He Was Singing This Song.*

If you're looking for a good cowboy song to sing at dances, this is as good a waltz tune as you're likely to find.

COWBOY JACK

Traditional

He was just a lonely cowboy
With a heart so brave and true;
He learned to love a maiden
With eyes of heavens' blue.

They learned to love each other
And had named their wedding day,
When a quarrel came between them,
And Jack he rode away.

He joined a band of cowboys
And tried to forget her name,
But out on the lonely prairie
She waits for him the same.

One night when work was finished
Just at the close of day,
Someone said, "Sing a song, Jack,
To drive dull cares away."

When Jack began his singing,
His mind did wander back,
For he sang of a maiden
Who waited for her Jack.

Your sweetheart waits for you, Jack,
Your sweetheart waits for you
Out on the lonely prairie
Where the skies are blue.

Jack left the camp next morning,
Breathing his sweetheart's name:
I'll go and ask forgiveness
For I know that I'm to blame.

He crossed the old Red River
And headed straight for town,
But his friends they sadly told him,
They'd laid his loved one down.

They said as she was dying,
She breathed her sweetheart's name,
And asked them with her last breath
To tell him when he came:

Your sweetheart waits for you, Jack,
Your sweetheart waits for you
Out on the lonely prairie
Where the skies are always blue.

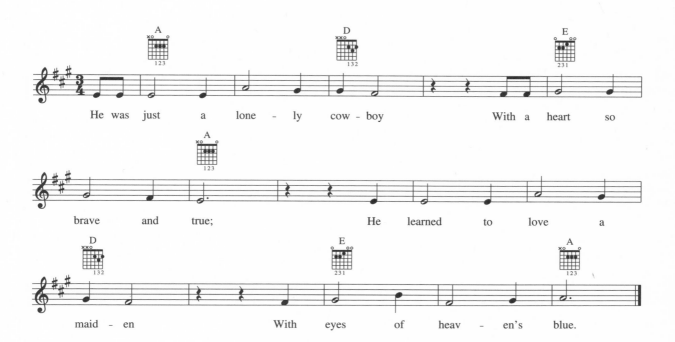

He was just a lone - ly cow - boy With a heart so brave and true; He learned to love a maid - en With eyes of heav - en's blue.

The Cowboy Life
(Is a Dreary, Dreary Life)

The "Cowboy Life," or "The Dreary Life" as it is sometimes called, probably came from a song around 1850 called "The Shantyman's Life." Jack Thorp first published the song in 1908 under the title "The Pecos Stream."

This song is another great example of how an old song gets changed into a cowboy song by changing its location. "The Shantyman's Life," a Maine woodsman's lament, had lyrics that went something like this:

The lumberman's life is a wearisome life,
Some say it's free from care.
But we chop down the pine from mornin' till night
In the middle of the forest so drear.

If you were to trace this song back to the Old Country, I bet you would find a similar song about the sea. Since sea chanteys were often turned into cowboy songs, the sailor was the cowboy's closest kin and followed the same parallels. "Bury Me Not in the Deep Blue Sea" became "Bury Me Not on the Lone Prairie," etc.

THE COWBOY LIFE
(IS A DREARY, DREARY LIFE)

Traditional
Arrangement and Adaptation by Don Edwards

The cowboy life is a dreary, dreary life;
Some say it's free from care.
Rounding up the cattle from morning till night
In the middle of the prairie so bare.

Half past four, the noisy cook will roar,
"Hey, boys! It's the breaking of day!"
Slowly we rise with sleepy-feeling eyes.
Has the short summer night passed away?

The cowboy life is a dreary, dreary life
From dawn till the setting sun.
And then his day's work it is not done
For there's still his night guard to go on.

The wolves and the owls with their terrifying howls
Disturb us in our midnight dream,
When we're laying in our slickers on a cold rainy night
Way over on the Pecos stream.

The cowboy life is a dreary, dreary life
All out in the midnight rain;
Punchin' cattle from morning till night
Way out on the Texas plains.

Spring sets in and our troubles all begin—
The weather being fierce and cold.
We're almost froze from the water on our clothes,
And the cattle we can scarcely hold.

The cowboy life is a mighty dreary life
All out in the sleet and snow
When wintertime comes, he begins to think,
Where did his summer wages go?

I once loved to roam, but now I stay at home.
All you punchers take my advice:
Sell your bridle and saddle; quit your roving and travel;
Tie onto a pretty little wife.

You can talk about your farms and your big-city charms;
You can talk about your silver and gold.
But the cowboy life is a dreary, dreary life
When you're driving through the heat and the cold.

The cowboy life is a dreary, dreary life
All out in the heat and cold.
While the rich man's sleeping on his velvet couch,
Dreaming of his silver and gold.

The cowboy life is a life of dust,
Though the cowboy laughs at fear.
But when he travels that last long trail
Is there no one to shed him a tear?

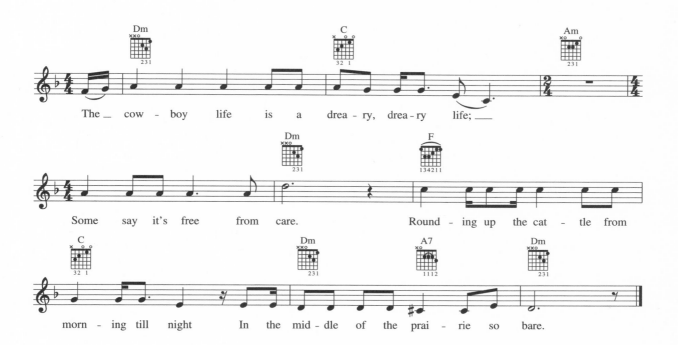

| Dm | | C | | Am | |

The _ cow - boy life is a drea - ry, drea - ry life; ___

| Dm | F |

Some say it's free from care. Round - ing up the cat - tle from

| C | Dm | A7 | Dm |

morn - ing till night In the mid - dle of the prai – rie so bare.

Katherine Field - 54.

Cowboy Love Song

Gail Gardner, the legendary Arizona cowboy who authored the famous "Tyin' Knots in the Devil's Tail," also wrote this song. It was first published in his book of poetry called the *Orejana Bull For Cowboys Only,* issued in 1935. Every time I'd pass through Prescott, Arizona, I'd ask about the song and if anyone remembered Gail singing it or what the melody was like, but to no avail. I even asked his grandson and my good friend, Gail Stieger, if he remembered a tune, but he couldn't come up with one at the time either. So in true cowboy style, I just wrote one of my own with my friend and western historian Paul Stone. We came up with the tune while attending a Western Music Association Festival in Tucson, Arizona, in 1989. There's a lot of inspiration out there in the desert.

COWBOY LOVE SONG

Lyrics by Gail Gardner
Music by Don Edwards and Paul C. Stone

See the sun a-comin' out
Behind the thunder showers.
Honey-chile, the mornin' loves you true.
Li'l raindrops glisten
On the painted injun flowers.
Honey-chile, the mornin' loves you true.

The muddy road is brown an' still
As far as you can see.
Honey-chile, the noontime loves you true,
A great big deer's a-watchin' us
Beneath that cedar tree.
Honey-chile, the noontime loves you true.

The sun is sinkin' through the trees
And leaves the clouds all red.
Honey-chile, the evenin' loves you true.
Just like I lights a nice warm fire
Before I goes to bed.
Honey-chile, the evenin' loves you true.

Old lady moon comes peekin' up
To see what she can see.
Honey-chile, the night time loves you true.
And finds you sittin' on a rock
So very close to me.
Honey-chile, I guess I loves you too.

At the Western Music Association in Tucson, Arizona, Don gets together with Riders in the Sky, Liz Masterson, Rusty Richards, Johnny Gimble, Patsy Montana, Hi Busse, and the Pfeiffer Bros.

See the sun a - com - in' out   Be - hind the thun - der - show'rs.

Hon - ey - chile, the morn - in'   loves you true.   Lit - tle rain-drops

glis - ten   On the paint - ed in - jun flow'rs.   Hon - ey - chile, the

morn - in'   loves you true.   The mud - dy road   is brown an' still   As

far   as you can   see.   Hon - ey - chile, ___ the noon - time   loves you

true.   A great big deer's   a - watch - in'   us   Be -

neath that ce - dar tree.   Hon - ey - chile, the noon-time   loves you true.

The Cowboy's Lament

"The Cowboy's Lament," "The Dying Cowboy," "Streets of Laredo"—they're all kin to the Irish ballad "The Unfortunate Rake." I have known this song for as long as I can remember, but it wasn't until years later that I heard a version by James Baker, who was known as "Iron Head" by his prison mates in the Texas State Penitentiary. This was the first African-based version I'd heard.

I believe the version printed here is one of the most obscure versions known lyric-wise. I have tried to mix both the Irish and the African influences into the same song.

USED BY PERMISSION: DICK CAPPLEMAN

Don relaxes at the West Fork Ranch near Fort Worth, Texas.

THE COWBOY'S LAMENT

Traditional
Arrangement and Adaptation by Don Edwards

So early one morning I rode o'er the ranches,
Rode o'er the ranches early one day.
I saw a young cowboy wrapped up in a blanket,
Wrapped up in a blanket as cold as the clay.

"I can see by your outfit, you are a cowboy."
These words he did say as I slowly rode by.
"They done gunned me down, boys, and run off and left me
Here on the prairie and left me to die.

"My friends and relations, I left them in Boston—
My parents knew not where I had roamed.
I first came to Texas a cowpuncher to be;
Now I'm shot in the breast, and hell is my doom.

"Now swing your ropes slowly, and ring your spurs lowly,
And play the dead march as you carry me along.
Take me to the graveyard and lay the sod o'er me—
I am a poor cowboy, and I know I done wrong.

"Go write a letter to my gray-headed mother
And break the news gently to my sisters, so dear.
But there is another who's as dear as my mother,
Who'd weep if she knew I was dying out here.

"Go gather around you a crowd of young cowboys,
And tell them the story of this my sad fate,
And tell them to stop all their drinking and gambling,
And all their wild rovings before it's too late.

"Get six cowboys to carry my coffin,
Six pretty whore gals to sing me a song.
Spread bunches of roses all over my coffin
So they can't smell me as they carry me along.

"So swing your ropes slowly, and ring your spurs lowly,
And play the dead march as you carry me along.
Take me to the graveyard and lay the sod o'er me—
I am a poor cowboy, and I know I done wrong."

Dm **C** **Dm** **C**

So ear - ly one morn-ing ___ I rode ___ o'er the ranch-es,

Dm **C** **A7**

Rode o'er the ranch - es ___ ear - ly one day. And I

Dm **C** **A7** **Dm**

saw a young cow - boy wrapped up in a blan-ket, ___ Wrapped

C **A7** **Dm**

up in a blan-ket ___ as cold as the clay.

Cow Town Blues

I've played in Cow Town (Fort Worth, Texas) for many years and have seen good times come and go. I remember how I used to play and sing at the White Elephant Saloon, while my friends Steve Murrin and Bobby Estes were producing a rodeo and Wild West show in the old coliseum. During my break at the saloon, I had a part in the Wild West show, where several cowboys and I would ride into the arena with the wagon and a few head of steers and sit around the campfire while I sang a few cowboy tunes. I would then mount up and ride out of the arena, and Steve and I would ride back over to the saloon for the next set. I would go back into the saloon and Steve would take both of the horses back to the arena. This went on three or four times a week.

One night, as I remember, we had had a few too many toddies, and after the arena show we rode back to the saloon. But this time, in keeping with the true tradition of the Old West, we just rode on in the saloon. The place was packed full of people, but I rode through the crowd and made my way to the stage, not thinking what a wreck this could have been. There were two steps up to the dance floor, so I jumped my horse up onto the floor, which was another mistake: I had forgotten about the ceiling fan, which is not a problem unless you happen to be a-horseback. Well, the fan just clipped my tall crown hat, and when I went to grab for it, my horse shied and pinned this dude up against the far wall. Didn't kick him or nothing, just sort of stepped on his Gucci loafers.

That dude called to the bartender, complaining that my horse had stepped on his fancy shoes and squashed one of his toes. Well, that old bartender, who was going right along with the whole thing, just leaned over the bar, looked that guy square in the eye, and said in his best Old West saloon lingo, "What the hell you doin' in here a-foot anyway?"

These were some of the best times until we got too many tourists coming, which of course was good and bad at the same time. It meant more rules about having horses on the streets and in the saloon. Things were changing, which was the reason for me writing this song. No sense elaborating on it any further except to tell you one more little story that came about during the 1994 Cowboy Poetry Gathering in Elko, Nevada, when my friend Wally McRae handed me this poem he had written about that little incident. I got to thinking how it would be a good idea to share it with you, so I called Wally at his ranch in Montana and told him about this book I was writing and would it be okay to include his poem. After we had visited about thirty minutes, he said he sure didn't mind if I used his poem (see p.50). Then in his usual unassuming way he said, "Had I known it was going to be turned out, I'da written it better." Thanks, Wally, but I think it's fine just the way it is.

COW TOWN BLUES

Don Edwards

I ain't got the blues, but I'm sure feelin' sad;
I ain't got the blues, but I'm sure feelin' sad;
I used to have nightmares, now even my daydreams are bad.

My old hometown ain't what she used to be;
My old hometown ain't what she used to be;
Too many near-sighted Henrys and Johnny-come-latelys for me.

Yodel

They're bringin' big city ways to a cowboy way of life;
They're bringin' big city ways to a cowboy way of life;
But their false ideals only bring us grief and strife.

Things have changed, it ain't just the beer that's cold;
Things have changed, it ain't just the beer that's cold;
No more bawlin' cattle, just the sound of rock 'n' roll.

Instrumental

I ain't got the blues, __ but I'm sure feel-in' sad; ___ I

ain't got the blues, __ but I'm sure feel - in' sad; ___ I

used to have night - mares, now e - ven my day - dreams are bad. ___

Them schemin' carpetbaggers are the ones to blame,
Tryin' to change our ways, the greedy fools are all the same;
The good days are gone, now nobody knows my name.

Now don't take me wrong, I still love Cow Town;
Oh, don't take me wrong, still a fool for old Cow Town;
But like some triflin' woman, she's gone and let me down.

Yodel

When a woman gets the blues, she hangs her head and cries;
When a woman gets the blues, she hangs her head and cries;
But when a cowboy gets blue, he saddles his horse and rides.

If you ever get the blues and don't know what to do;
If you ever get the blues and don't know what to do;
Just saddle your horse and ride the whole world through.

"In without Knocking"
(a modern update)

A Poem by Wallace D. McRae
Rocker Six Cattle Co.

Don Edwards rode into the barroom,
Booted, spurred, and hatted up,
Just to have a small libation
From what's known as Bacchus Cup.

It may not have been the smartest thing
That Don had ever done.
But the record's clear. The precedent's
Been set on cowboy fun.

And ridin' into bottle joints
Is a part of Western lore;
Though it ain't been done much lately,
It's sure as hell been done before!

And Fort Worth is still a cow town
Just like it's always been.
So hosses have the right of way;
To change *that* law would be a sin.

But Donald's hoss trod on some yuppie
Who was in Gucci loafers shod,
And the yuppie told the barkeep,
"I'm gonna sue your ass, by god,

" 'Cause that redneck's horse trod on my foot,
Which did my body grievous harm.
My lawyer will be calling you.
To coin a phrase, 'you've bought the farm.' "

The barkeep said, "Be careful, wimp,
Or you might make my day.
'Sides, what the hell you doin'
Afoot here anyway?"

End of the Trail

Like the poem "Lolita" in the novel *Curley,* "End of the Trail" appears in the novel as well. The novel and the poems were written by Captain Roger Pocock, a British military officer who had a flair for the American West. When I set the poem to music, it came out with kind of a bluesy western feel. What a coincidence! At any rate, I think this is a pretty good put-together.

A man who is very much in demand for his musical abilities, Don performs here with the Fort Worth Symphony Orchestra.

END OF THE TRAIL

Lyrics by Roger Pocock
Music by Don Edwards

Soh, dogies, Soh,
The water's handy heah,
The grass is plenty neah,
And all the stars a-sparkle
Bekaze we drive no mo'—
We drive no mo'.

The long trail ends today;
The long trail ends today;
The punchers go to play,
And all you weary cattle
May sleep in peace for sure—
May sleep in peace for sure—
Sleep, sleep for sure.

Soh, cattle, Soh!
The moon can't bite you heah,
Nor punchers fright you neah
An' you-all will be beef befo'
We need you any mo'—
We need you any mo'!

The long trail ends today;
The long trail ends today;
The punchers go to play,
And all you weary cattle
May sleep in peace for sure—
May sleep in peace for sure—
Sleep, sleep for sure.

G

Soh, _____ do - gies, Soh, _____

C   C7   G

The wa-ter's hand-y _____ heah,   The grass ____ is ____ plen-ty neah,

D7   C7   Bb   Ab

And   all   the stars a - spark - le   Be - kaze we drive _____ no mo' ___

G   C7   G

___   We   drive   no   mo'.

Katherine Field - 35

53

Good-bye, Old Paint

Black cowhands were hard workers, dedicated, and unquestionably some of the finest singers in the cow business. Charley Willis, born in Milam County, Texas, worked breaking horses for E. J. Morris after the Civil War. He took to the trail in 1871 with one of the Snyder Brothers' herds, going north to Wyoming and ending in Cheyenne. Charlie learned this song somewhere along the way.

Famous XIT cowboy and fiddle player Jesse Morris learned to play the fiddle from a black cowhand, Jerry Neely, and has the oldest-known version of "Good-bye, Old Paint." Morris recorded the song for the Library of Congress in 1947.

This version is one of my put-togethers, a combination of "Ridin' Old Paint" and "Good-bye, Old Paint." Some of the verses are forms of the above plus songs like "My Horses Ain't Hungry," "Jack O' Diamonds," "Rye Whiskey," and "The Wagoner's Lad." You can call it whatever you want. You can even take my lead and make up your own song. Good luck!

GOOD-BYE, OLD PAINT

Traditional
Adaptation by Don Edwards

I'm ridin' Old Paint and leadin' Old Dan;
I'm goin' to Montana to throw the houlihan,
Where they feed in the coulees, and they water in the draw;
Their tails are all matted; their backs are all raw.

Chorus:
Good-bye, Old Paint, I'm leavin' Cheyenne.
Good-bye, Old Paint, I'm leavin' Cheyenne.
I'm leavin' Cheyenne; I'm off to Montana.
Good-bye Old Paint, I'm leavin' Cheyenne.

I'm leavin' this country to stay for awhile
Across the wide prairie a many a long mile.
Well, it's dark, cold, and dreary—the moon sheds no light—
And my horses won't travel that dark road at night.

Chorus

Get down from your horses and feed them some hay,
And sit down beside me for as long as you'll stay.
My horses ain't hungry; they won't eat your hay.
So fare thee well, Molly, I'm goin' away.

Chorus

Fare thee well, Molly, I'm leavin' Cheyenne.
Good-bye, my little Doney, my ponies won't stand.
Oh, the last time I saw her was late in the fall;
She was wavin' good-bye then started to bawl.

Chorus

My foot's in the stirrup and my bridle in my hand;
Old Paint's a good pony; he paces when he can.
I'll spread down my blanket on the green grassy ground
Where the horses and cattle are grazin' all around.

Chorus

When I die, take my saddle from the wall,
Put it on my paint pony, and lead him from the stall.
Tie my bones to his back and face us to the West,
And we'll ride the wide prairie that we loved the best.

Chorus

I'm rid - in' Old Paint and lead - in' old Dan; I'm go - in' to Mon -

tan - a to throw the hou - li - han, Where they feed in the cou - lees, and they

wat - er in the draw; Their tails are all mat - ted, their backs are all

Chorus

raw. Good - bye, Old Paint, I'm leav - in' Chey - enne. Good -

bye, Old Paint, I'm leav - in' Chey - enne. I'm leav - in' Chey - enne; I'm

off to Mon - tan - a. Good - bye, Old Paint, I'm leav - in' Chey - enne.

Gypsy Davey

This song has both English and Scottish origins. One of the earliest versions is child ballad #200, "The Gypsy Laddie." In the Old World versions, the Gypsy lad is usually caught with the lady and dies for taking her away. In American versions, the Lady and the Gypsy become lovers and make their escape from the wicked Lord.

Here we have a cowboy version I didn't know existed until I heard Harry Jackson do it. Harry has a great collection of cowboy songs on Folkways called *Harry Jackson, The Cowboy: His Songs, Ballads, and Brag Talk*. Harry's version is called "Clayton Boone," and Woodie Guthrie also has another cowboy version on a Library of Congress recording AAPS L1.

I play this song using a drop D tuning. To get this tuning, just lower the low E string to D. This is the easiest of the non-standard tunings.

GYPSY DAVEY

Cowboy version by Harry Jackson
Arrangement and Adaptation by Don Edwards

'Twas way out in New Mexico
Along the Spanish line,
I went to work for Diamond Joe,
A man well past his prime,
A man well past his prime.

Well, he rides in, and he asks of me,
"What happened to my lady?"
I says to him, "She's quit your range
And run with the Gypsy Davey,
Run with the Gypsy Davey."

"Go saddle for me my buckskin horse
With the silver-mounted saddle;
Point out to me their fresh-laid tracks,
And after them I'll travel,
After them I'll ride."

He rode until the midnight moon,
Till he saw their campfire gleaming;
He heard the Gypsy's big guitar
And the voice of his lady singing
The song of the Gypsy Dave.

There in the light of the camping fire,
He saw her fair face beaming,
Her heart in tune to the big guitar
And the voice of her Gypsy singing.

"Have you forsaken your house and home,
Have you forsaken your baby?
Have you forsaken my silver and gold
To ride with the Gypsy Davey,
To ride with Gypsy Dave?"

"Yes, I've forsaken my house and home
To go with the Gypsy Davey,
And I'll forsake your silver and gold
But not my blue-eyed babe.

"Last night I slept with a mean old man
In golden rooms so stately;
Tonight I'll sleep on the cold hard ground
Beside my lover Davey,
And I'll ride with my Gypsy Dave,
And sing with Gypsy Davey.

"He's no Gypsy, my husband," said she,
"He's the lord of the free land all over,
And I will stay till my dying day—
My heart's with the Gypsy Rover,
With my singing Gypsy Rover."

'Twas way out in New Mex - i - co ___ A - long the Span - ish line, I

went to work for Dia - mond Joe, A man well past his prime, A

man well past his prime. Well, he rides in, and he asks of me, "What

hap - pened to my la - dy?" I says to him, "She's quit your range And

run with the Gyp - sy Da - vey, ___ Run with the Gyp - sy Da - vey."

The Habit

This was originally written as a poem by Berton Braley, but it has been recorded many times as a song. It has appeared in song folios by the Arkansas Woodchopper and several others over the years. It was even recorded by the Sons of the Pioneers under the title "Rolling Stone" on a Standard Radio Transcription in the 1930s. I recorded my own version of the song on my album *Chant of the Wanderer*, but I have since written a little bit different tune and added a little refrain. It has become an audience favorite.

THE HABIT

Lyrics by Berton Braley
Music by Don Edwards

Recite:
I've settled down quite frequent and I says, says I,
"I'll never travel further till I comes to die."
But the wind, it sorta chuckles, "Why, o' course you will."
And sure enough, I does it 'cause I jes' can't keep still.

Sing:
I've beat my way wherever any winds have blown;
I've bummed along from Reno down to San Antone;
From Tucson up to Frisco, over plains and hills;
For once you get The Habit, you jes' can't keep still.

Chorus:
I ride wherever the wind blows
Drifting like a tumbleweed;
I'm just a wanderin' troubadour;
My guitar and a song is all I need.

I've seen a lot o' places where I'd like to stay;
But I gets to feelin' restless an' I'm on my way;
I was never meant for settin' on my own door sill,
An' once you get The Habit, you jes' can't keep still.

Chorus

I've been in rich men's houses, and I've been in jail;
But when it's time for leavin', I jes hits the trail.
I'm a human bird of passage, and the song I trill
Is "Once you get The Habit, why you jes' can't keep still."

Chorus

The sun is sorta coaxin', and the road is clear,
And the wind is singin' ballads that I got to hear.
It ain't no use to argue when you feel the thrill,
For once you get The Habit, why you jes' can't keep still.

Traveling a-horseback to the Grand Tetons in Wyoming, Don admires the country he's traveling through.

I've beat my way wher-ev-er _____ an-y winds have blown; I've
bummed a-long _ from Re - no _____ down to San An - tone; _
From Tuc - son up to Fris - co, o - ver plains _ and hills; For
once you get The Hab - it, _____ you jes' can't keep still. I
ride wher-ev - er the wind _ blows _____ Drift - ing like a tum - ble -
weed; I'm just a wan - der - in' trou - ba - dour; _____
— My gui - tar and a song is all I need.

"Don"

WADDIE MITCHELL

DON

A Poem by Waddie Mitchell

For several years now, my best friend and compadre, Waddie Mitchell, and I have been working and traveling together all over the country and even in Europe with our show "The Bard and the Balladeer," a mixture of music, poetry, and storytelling. Although our material, both classic and contemporary, deals with the life and times of the cowboy, we are not immune to the trials and tribulations of modern society.

Instead of burdening you with the whys and wherefores of my opinionated manner, I thought I'd just let Waddie's poetic observations speak for themselves.

Waddie Mitchell and Don Edwards—"The Bard and the Balladeer"— team up together at Westfest in Red River, New Mexico, June 1991.

I saw emotions well up in him
As she pointed with a grin,
Saying, "Sign there at the bottom, please,"
While handing him a pen.

I could tell he needed venting
Or I feared he would explode;
I dug in for the onslaught
While he proceeded to unload
His opinions on that young gal;
How this country should be run;
How lawyers should be something scarce;
And how business should be done.

How you didn't need no contracts
When a man's word was an oath,
And it was worth a lot more
Than a paper signed by both.

How at one time giant deals were made
With the shaking of a hand,
And you could bet your life and livelihood
On the promise of a man.

How neighbor meant a whole lot more
Than simply living near;
And all could walk the streets at night
Without a nagging fear.

How citizens could arm themselves
And crimes weren't blamed on guns
But on crimesters that committed them,
And bad ones still got hung.

How a shyster's reign was short-lived
'Cause good folks would run them off,
And thugs and thieves would land in jail
'Cause judges weren't so soft.

How divorce was near unheard of,
And kids were raised at home;
How there weren't no old-folks' centers
'Cause we took care of our own.

How cars and tools weren't throw away
'Cause things were built to last.
How a man would tip his hat out
On the street when ladies passed.

The young gal's eyes were glazin'
As she stood there in a stare.
I was gettin' kind of antsy
And was wantin' out of there—

But he went on about . . . fat cowboys—
How they once were hard and lean
Before they all used trucks and goosenecks—
And how strikes were seldom seen.

How you didn't need no resumé
To land yourself a job;
How public office wasn't just
A legal way to rob;

How if you were able-bodied
Then you found yourself some work,
And welfare wasn't handed out
To lazy bums that shirk.

How doctors still made house calls
That didn't cost an arm and leg;
How an appointment with your banker
Wouldn't dictate that you beg.

How insurance was affordable
'Cause people weren't so apt to sue;
How you didn't expect ten times more
Than you were rightf'ly due.

How taxes didn't break ya
'Cause we all paid our fair share,
And there weren't folks spendin' full time
Finding all the loop holes there.

How the public trough weren't feedin'
Near as many bureaucrats;
And when the BLM was small—
But now they're like a swarm of gnats.

How credit cards are rip-offs;
How voters have got to learn
That you can't pay off a deficit
If you spend more than you earn.

How if somebody is strugglin'
We should lend a helping hand.
How it ain't right that some foreigners
Are buying up this land.

He'd gone on for twenty minutes
Before he took hisself a breath.
I thought I'd better jump in now
'Fore he talks that gal to death.

So, I said, "Don, you're right on all counts,
But we've really got to go—
And if you don't sign that there contract,
We can't rent the video!"

Hard Times Blues

I wrote this song based on an old song called "Hard Times" that appeared in John Lomax's 1910 version of *Cowboy Songs*. I have never been able to find out where it came from before then. I rewrote it to relay my personal sentiments of a fast-decaying modern society, especially here in our own country where greed and materialism takes precedence over all else.

We've got a great country here with good, honest, hard-working people. It's just too bad the government doesn't know it. They're doing their damndest to destroy the very heart and soul of this country, so I think it's time we all came out of our comas and did something about it.

Most of my songs aren't about gloom and doom, but it wouldn't be honest to just sing about "Happy Trails" and "Home on the Range" either. We all need to feel the sting of the quirt and the jab of a spur rowel occasionally.

USED BY PERMISSION: DICK CAPPLEMAN

HARD TIMES BLUES
Don Edwards

Come listen awhile, and I'll sing you a song
Concerning the times; it won't take very long.
We fought and we died for the land of the free;
Now the home of the brave is all ate up with greed.

Chorus:
Now it's Hard Times, Hard Times, Hard Times I cry;
If Hard Times don't kill me, I'll live till I die.

Since greed has grown to be such a fashion,
I believe in my soul it'll ruin the whole nation;
There's too many rules and too many laws,
Bad men in high places and good men on the dodge.

Chorus

Now there is the lawyer, you'll plainly see,
He'll plead your case for a very large fee;
He'll law you and tell you that the wrong side is right
And make you believe that a black horse is white.

Chorus

There's the politician, so honest we're told,
Whatever he sells you, my friend, you are sold;
Believe what I tell you and don't be surprised;
He's got a handful of gimme and a mouthful of lies.

Chorus

I hate the government, the revenuers, too.
What in the world is a poor boy to do?
They'll pick all your pockets; your clothes they will sell
For the almighty dollar. Damn 'em to hell!

Chorus

Come lis-ten a-while, and I'll sing you a song Con-cern-ing the times; it won't take ver-y long. We fought and we died for ___ the land of the free; Now the home of the brave is all ate up with greed. Now it's Hard Times, Hard Times, Hard Times I cry; ___ ___ If Hard Times don't kill me, I'll live till I die. ___

Chorus

I Wanted to Die in the Desert

I've been aware of this poem for many years, and have found it in many western and cowboy poetry collections.

As you may or may not be aware, I am a researcher as well as an entertainer. I enjoy looking into the origins of my songs and poetry and am obsessed with finding the authors. This can lead to a lot of very interesting and useful material, but in most cases, the author can't be identified and, in some cases, doesn't want to be.

I would like to find the author of this poem that I've put to music. It's possible that it could have been a self-written obituary. It has also been rumored on several occasions that it might have been written by Curley Fletcher, but we don't know for sure.

I WANTED TO DIE IN THE DESERT

Author Unknown
Arrangement and Adaptation by Don Edwards

I wanted to die in the desert—
I planned it for twenty years—
Alone with my God and my conscience,
And not a sky-pilot near.

I meant what I said when I doped it,
For it threw a spell over me.
Its mesas, its sand, and its deadness—
It was the place I wanted to be.

I've roamed, I've traveled all over it;
I've stood on the brink of hell;
I wooed it, I coaxed it, I fought it,
And was caught in its deadly spell.

I said when I croaked that I'd go
To the desert to find my hole,
With snakes and coyotes to watch over me,
And my headstone a lone yucca pole.

But the death I've cheated so often
Has pulled its freight into town,
And I can't get back to the desert;
I'm broke—not a penny—I'm down.

Life is a burden and not worth the while,
So I'll play the ace up my sleeve.
It's poison—quick stuff—and Saint Peter;
Adios to the world I leave.

Just throw my old hide in the cactus,
Out where the desert wind moans;
For I wanted to die in the desert,
Where the buzzards would peck at my bones.

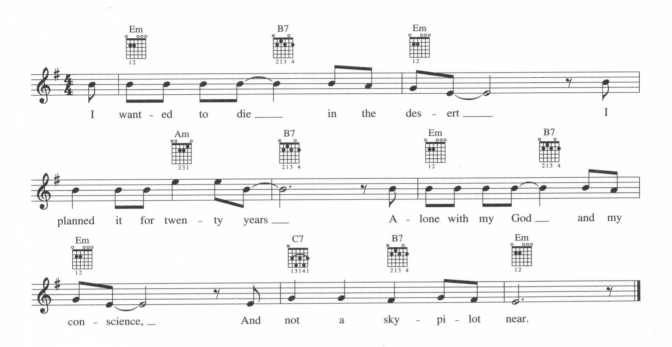

I want-ed to die ____ in the des - ert ____ I
planned it for twen - ty years ____ A - lone with my God ____ and my
con - science, ___ And not a sky - pi - lot near.

I'd Like to Be in Texas

Another one of my favorite old cowboy songs. It was first recorded by Vernon Dalhart in 1926. The first recording of it that I ever heard was by Slim Critchlow. In fact, it was from his recording that I first learned the song.

The song was most likely written by some old-time cowboy and not by Carl Copeland and Jack Williams, who were credited as writers and assigned a copyright in 1935. I'm inclined to believe this because two stanzas of the song were found in an unpublished play written by Andy Adams, an old cowboy famous for his classic book *The Log of a Cowboy*, 1903. It was common practice in the 1920s, '30s, and '40s, when sheet music and song folios were at their peak of popularity, for song sharks to put their names on what were believed to be old traditional songs. People like Curley Fletcher can attest to this practice because Nat Vincent and Fred Howard put their copyright on "The Strawberry Roan."

The first sheet music of "I'd Like to Be in Texas" was published and copyrighted by Lou Fishback in 1927. He was singing the song and selling sheet music in the Blackstone Hotel in Fort Worth, Texas, during that time.

I recorded the song in my first cowboy song anthology, *Songs of the Cowboy*, in 1985. I later recorded the song again on my first Warner/Western, album *Songs of the Trail*. Nobody cared about my little self-published book and tape; but when I signed with Warner Brothers, they didn't let the dust settle before they were wanting money. What these folks don't understand is that singing and playing cowboy music pays about the same as cowboyin' does—ain't none of us ever goin' to get rich. The real rewards come from living the life and singing the songs.

It was because of this song that I became friends with Walt Larue. Walt's a fine singer of cowboy songs—a wonderful artist, a sure 'nough cowboy and one of the well-known stuntmen in Hollywood. This song is one of his favorites.

I've added an additional verse at the end of the song that I had never heard in American versions. I discovered it on a recording by popular Australian folk singer Tex Morton. I have been unable to find its origin, but it sure was a great find. It was sent to me by my Australian friend, singer, and poet Jim Haynes.

I'D LIKE TO BE IN TEXAS

Traditional

In the lobby of a big hotel in New York town one day
Sat a bunch of fellows telling yarns to pass the time away.
They told of places where they'd been and different things they'd seen;
Some preferred Chicago town while others, New Orleans.

In a corner in an old armchair sat a man whose hair was gray;
He listened to them eagerly to what they had to say.
They asked him where he'd like to be; his clear old voice did ring,
"I'd like to be in Texas for the roundup in the spring."

Chorus:
"I can see the cattle grazing o'er the hills at early morn;
I can see the campfires smoking at the breaking of the dawn;
I can hear the broncos neighing; I can hear the cowboy sing;
I'd like to be in Texas for the roundup in the spring."

They sat and listened carefully to each word he had to say;
They knew the old man sitting there had been a top hand in his day.
They asked him for a story of his life out on the plains.
Slowly he removed his hat then quietly began:

"I've seen 'em stampede o'er the hills till you'd think they'd never stop;
I've seen 'em run for miles and miles until their leaders dropped;
I was foreman of a cow ranch—the calling of a king;
I'd like to be in Texas for the roundup in the spring."

Chorus

"I'd like to sleep my last long sleep with mother earth for bed,
My saddle for a pillow, the bright stars overhead;
Then I could hear the last stampede, the songs the rivers sing,
Way back down in Texas when they roundup in the spring."

Lee's Ferry

I first heard this song sung by Glenn Ohrlin. I'd always wanted to meet Glenn because I had heard of him for many years as a rodeo cowboy and folksinger. But I was particularly interested in his knowledge of cowboy songs. I got to meet and become friends with Glenn, thanks to the Cowboy Poetry Gathering in Elko, Nevada. I hope he didn't mind me picking his brain every time I saw him, but I think he is the perfect example of what a true cowboy singer ought to be.

The song was written by Arizona cowboy singer Romaine Lowdermilk, probably best known for his song "The Big Corral." My regret is that I never had the chance to meet him.

Lee's Ferry is on the Colorado River, the only crossing place in northern Arizona. There's a lot of history and interesting country around there. For more detailed information about the song and the area, read Glenn Ohrlin's book *The Hell-Bound Train*. As for Romaine Lowdermilk, you need to read chapter nine in John I. White's book *Get Along, Little Dogies*.

LEE'S FERRY

Romaine Lowdermilk

Come all you rovin' cowboys, bound on these western plains;
Come all you rovin' cowboys, we'll go back home again.
We'll see old friends and neighbors and those we love so dear;
We'll cross over Lee's Ferry-o and go back home this year.

"We will, we will," they all did say, "when the fall roundup is o'er.
We'll visit scenes of olden days and see old friends once more;
We'll see old friends and neighbors and those we love so dear;
We'll cross over Lee's Ferry-o and go back home this year."

It's easy for to make a vow; it's easy to forget.
Those boys are old and graying now, and they're cowpunchin' yet.
Never saw their friends and neighbors or those they loved so dear;
We never crossed Lee's Ferry-o to go back home that year.

Don pauses for a photograph with friends Baxter Black, Waddie Mitchell, and Chris LeDoux at Westfest in Copper Mountain, Colorado.

Come all you ro - vin' cow - boys, bound on _____ these west-ern _____ plains; Come all you ro - vin' cow - boys, we'll go ___ back home a - gain. We'll see old friends and neigh - bors and those we love so dear; We'll cross o - ver Lee's Fer - ry - o ___ and go ___ back home this year.

Little Joe, the Wrangler

No collection of cowboy songs would be complete without including "Little Joe, the Wrangler." Jack Thorp said he wrote the song on a paper bag beside a campfire, while trailing a herd of cattle from Chimney Lake, New Mexico, to Higgins, Texas, in 1898. On the return trip, he sang it for the first time at Uncle Johnny Root's store and saloon in Weed, New Mexico, to the tune of "Little Old Log Cabin in the Lane." Weed was also the birthplace of western musician and movie actor Cactus Mack, born August 8, 1899. Cactus Mack played fiddle for Ray Whitley's Six Bar Cowboys and played guitar with singing cowboy star Fred Scott and the Cimarron Boys.

There have been many parodies of this song, including "Little Joe, the Wrangler's Sister Nell" and "Little Bunch of Cactus on the Wall." Both songs were said to be written by Thorp, but he only claimed the latter. Another song that became quite popular was "Cowboy Jack's Last Ride," which took its theme from "Little Joe, the Wrangler" and the melody from "Cowboy Jack." There was also a railroad parody called "The Little Red Caboose Behind the Train."

LITTLE JOE, THE WRANGLER

N. Howard "Jack" Thorp

Little Joe, the wrangler, will wrangle nevermore;
His days with the remuda, they are o'er.
'Twas a year ago last April when he rode into our camp—
A little Texas stray and all alone.

'Twas late in the evening he rode up to the herd
On a little Texas pony he called Chaw,
With brogan shoes and overalls, a tougher-looking kid
You never in your life had ever saw.

His saddle was a Southern kack built many years ago;
An OK spur on one foot lightly swung,
With his hot roll in a cotton sack and loosely tied behind
And a canteen from his saddle horn was slung.

He said he had to leave his home, his Pa had married twice,
And his new Ma whipped him every day or two;
So he saddled up old Chaw one night and lit a shuck this way;
Now he's trying hard to paddle his own canoe.

He said if we would give him work, he'd do the best he could,
Though he didn't know straight-up about a cow.
So the boss he cut him out a mount and kindly put him on
For he sorter liked the little kid somehow.

He learned to jingle horses and to know them one and all
And to round 'em up by daylight if he could,
To follow the chuck wagon and to always hitch the team
And help the Cocinero rustle wood.

Lit - tle Joe, the wran - gler, _____ will wran - gle nev - er - more; ___ His

days with the re - mu - da, they are o'er. _ 'Twas a year a - go ___ last A - pril _ when he

rode in - to our camp _ A lit - tle Tex - as stray and all a - lone.

We'd driven to Red River, the weather being fine;
We were camped out on the south side in a bend
When a Norther commenced to blowing, and we doubled up our guard,
For it took all hands to hold the cattle in.

Little Joe, the wrangler, was called out with the rest,
And though the kid had scarcely reached the herd,
When the cattle they stampeded like a hailstorm, long they fled,
And we were all a-riding for the lead.

'Midst the streaks of lightning there was one horse up ahead
Trying to stop the leaders in their speed;
It was Little Joe, the wrangler, with a slicker o'er his head;
He was riding Old Blue Rocket in the lead.

We finally got 'em milling and kind of quieted down
And the extra guard back to the wagon rode,
But there was one a-missing and we knew it at a glance
'Twas our little Texas stray, poor Wrangler Joe.

Next morning just at sunup, we found where Rocket fell,
Down by a washout twenty feet below,
Beneath his horse, mashed to a pulp, his spurs had rung the knell
For our little Texas stray, poor Wrangler Joe.

Lonesome Trail Blues

Of all the cattle trails, the Chisholm was probably the most famous and had more songs written about it than any other, "The Old Chisholm Trail" being one of the most authentic of all cowboy songs. I wrote this song after reading a story about river crossings in J. Frank Dobie's *The Longhorns*.

In June of 1871, a trail herd of some two thousand steers led by Colonel Todd reached the Red River to find it flooded and impossible to cross. Todd and his hands tried to hold the cattle on the south side of the river until the rain stopped and the river went down, but they didn't plan on it raining for ten days. Other herds coming up behind were forced to wait as well. Some dozen herds and nearly twenty-five thousand cattle were starting to back up, and soon the grass would be overgrazed, and the threat of stampedes became more real every day.

Todd finally made the decision to push the herd into the river, but without anyone in front to keep the leaders moving, they began to swim in "the fatal circle." Todd hollered out to one of his hands, a young boy by the name of Jimmy Foster, to ride into the river and try to break up the jam of milling cattle.

Jimmy stripped down to his long handles and mounted a big horse called Jack Moore. He rode out to the herd, got off his horse and onto the backs of the cattle like a lumberjack would do in breaking up a log jam. He finally made it to one of the biggest steers in the bunch, mounted and rode him to the far shore where, just before reaching the bank, he slid into the water and floated downstream to his horse. It must have been about nine o'clock in the morning when Jim finally got out on land with no hat, no saddle, and no one to help him. He held the herd together till nearly sundown. It was surely a miracle that they didn't lose a single steer in the incident.

LONESOME TRAIL BLUES

Don Edwards

Went up the trail in '71.
Went up the trail in '71.
With two thousand steers, the drive had just begun.
Went up the trail in '71.

It was a long and lonesome go.
It was a long and lonesome go.
Through mesquite, thorns, and thickets, oh, how the wind did blow.
It was a long and lonesome go.

The sweat and the dust burned your eyes.
The sweat and the dust burned your eyes.
As far as you could see, the dusty billows rise.
The sweat and the dust burned your eyes.

Then dark clouds covered up the sun.
Then dark clouds covered up the sun.
The rain come upon us, and our troubles soon begun.
The dark clouds covered up the sun.

Ten days the rain it never stopped.
Ten days the rain it never stopped.
A stampede every night till you'd think them steers would drop.
Ten days the rain it never stopped.

The Red River flowed at full flood.
The Red River flowed at full flood.
It rolled fast and deep like the Mississippi mud.
The Red River flowed at full flood.

A dozen herds a-waitin' for the river to go down.
A dozen herds a-waitin' for the river to go down.
Soon twenty thousand cattle would overgraze the ground.
A dozen herds a-waitin' for the river to go down.

Went up the trail in sev-en-ty-one. ___ Went

up the trail in sev-en-ty-one. ___ With two thou-sand steers, the

drive had just ___ be-gun. Went up the trail in sev-en-ty-one. ___

The boss hollers, "Drive the lead steers in."
The boss hollers, "Drive the lead steers in."
Then halfway across in a fatal circle swimmin',
The boss hollered, "Drive the lead steers in."

Jimmy Foster was a brave cowhand.
Jimmy Foster was a brave cowhand.
He walked across the herd like it was a big log jam.
Jimmy Foster was a brave cowhand.

He rode a big lead steer across.
He rode a big lead steer across.
The others they soon followed; not a single steer was lost
As he rode that big lead steer across.

He held the herd from mornin' till sundown.
He held the herd from mornin' till sundown.
With no saddle clothes nor help, and almost nearly
    drowned.
He held the herd from mornin' till sundown.

I got them lonesome trail blues.
Oh, I got them lonesome trail blues.
I'll quit this cowboy life; I tell you I am through.
I got them lonesome trail blues.

It was hard times along the Chisholm Trail.
It was hard times along the Chisholm Trail.
It's a wonder that we lived long enough to tell this tale.
It was hard times along the Chisholm Trail.

I'm goin' where it never rains nor snows.
I'm goin' where it never rains nor snows.
Goin' where the climate suits my clothes, poor boy.
Goin' where it never rains nor snows.

The Long Road West

This is a poem written by Henry Herbert Knibbs that I set to music. Although Knibbs's poetry hasn't been set to music as often as Badger Clark's has, he is still one of the greatest of all cowboy poets.

"The Long Road West" appears in Knibbs's *Songs of the Trail,* a rare book of poetry printed by the Houghton Mifflin Company of Boston in 1920. I named my first Warner/Western album after this book.

What inspired me about this poem is the kinship of the hobo, the sailor, and the cowboy, and how they all share the same love for . . .

> *Valley, range, and high trail,*
> *   mesa, butte, and river,*
> *Sun across the lowlands,*
> *   rolling down to rest.*

and their strong belief that . . .

> *There'll always be a skyline,*
> *   running on forever,*
> *running on forever,*
> *   down that long road West.*

THE LONG ROAD WEST

Lyrics by Henry Herbert Knibbs
Music by Don Edwards

Once I heard a hobo, singing by the tie-trail
Squatting by the red rail rusty with the dew:
Singing of the firelight, singing of the high trail
Singing to the morning as the dawn broke through:

Refrain:
"Saddle, rail, or packsack—any way you take it:
Choose a pal and try him, but on your own is best.
Sand, clay, or cinders—any way to make it.
Looking for tomorrow down the long road West."

Far across the ranges, over where the sea swings—
Battering the raw ledge, booming up the sand:
There I heard a sailor telling what the sea sings,
Sings to every sailor when he longs for land:

Refrain:
"When you've saved your cash, and when you've done your hitch, sir;
—Holystone and hardtack, buckle to the test—
When you're back in port, and your feet begin to itch, sir,
Think about tomorrow and the long road West."

Slowly came a cowboy riding 'round the night herd;
Silver was the starlight, slender was the moon:
Then I heard him singing, lonely as a nightbird,
Pony's head a-nodding to the queer old tune:

Refrain:
"Wind, rain, and sunshine—every kind of weather—
Sweating on the mesa, freezing on the crest.
Me and just my shadow jogging on together,
Jogging on together down the long road West."

Lazy was the cool stream slipping through the far light,
Shadowing the buckthorn high along the hill,
When I heard a bird sing softly in the starlight,
Singing in the evening when the trees were still:

Refrain:
"Valley, range, and high trail, mesa, butte, and river,
Sun across the lowlands, rolling down to rest.
There'll always be the skyline, running on forever,
Running on forever down the long road West."

Once I heard a ho-bo, sing-in' by the tie-trail Squat-ting by the red rail

rust-y with the dew: Sing-ing of the fire-light,

sing-ing of the high trail Sing-ing to the morn-ing as the dawn broke through:

"Sad-dle, rail, or pack-sack — an-y-way you take it: Choose a pal and try him, but

on your own is best. Sand, clay, or cin-ders —

an-y-way to make it. Look-ing for to-mor-row down the long road West."

'Longside the Santa Fe Trail

One of my favorite cowboy books is Jules Verne Allen's *Cowboy Lore,* which contains this song. I also have a recording of Jules singing the song. The first time I ever heard it sung live was by Glenn Ohrlin at the Cowboy Poetry Gathering in Elko, Nevada. He sure can get a lot of mileage out of this song; I've never heard it done better.

I recorded a version of it in my second book-and-tape anthology, *Guitars and Saddle Songs.* The Department of Interior National Park Service used my recording of the song in their film *All's Set on the Santa Fe National Historic Trail,* produced by Ladder Films of New Mexico.

'LONGSIDE THE SANTA FE TRAIL

James Grafton Rogers

Say, pard, have you sighted a schooner
A-hittin' the Santa Fe Trail?
They may be here Monday or sooner
With a water keg tied on the tail.
There's Daddy and Ma on the mule seat,
And somewhere along by the way,
A tow-headed gal on a pinto
A-janglin' for old Santa Fe.
Yo-ho-oh
A-janglin' for old Santa Fe.

I saw her ride down the arroyo
Way back on the Arkansas sand
With a smile like an acre of sunflowers
And a little brown quirt in her hand.
She straddled her pinto so airy
And rode like she carried the mail,
And her eyes near set fire to the prairie
'Longside the Santa Fe Trail.
Yo-ho-oh
'Longside the Santa Fe Trail.

I know a gal down on the border
That I'd ride to El Paso to sight;
I'm acquainted with the high-steppin' order
And I've sometimes kissed some gals good night.
But, Lord, they're all just ruffles and beadin'
And afternoon tea by the pail
Compared to the kind of stampedin'
That I got on the Santa Fe Trail.
Yo-ho-oh
That I got on the Santa Fe Trail.

I don't know her name, and the prairie
When it comes to one gal, it's pretty wide.
But it's shorter from Hell to Hilary
Than it is on this Santa Fe ride.
I guess I'll make Cedars by sundown,
And I'll camp somewhere in a swale;
I'll come on a gal on a pinto
'Longside the Santa Fe Trail.
Yo-ho-oh
'Longside the Santa Fe Trail.

Say, pard, have you sight-ed a schoon-er _____ A - hit-tin' ____ the

San - ta Fe Trail? They may be here Mon-day or

soon-er _____ With a wa-ter keg tied on the tail. There's

Dad-dy and Ma on the mule __ seat, _____ And some-where a-long _

__ by the way, A tow-head-ed gal on a

pin-to _____ A - jang-lin' for old San-ta Fe. Yo-

ho - oh _____ A - jang-lin' for old San-ta Fe.

Minstrel of the Range

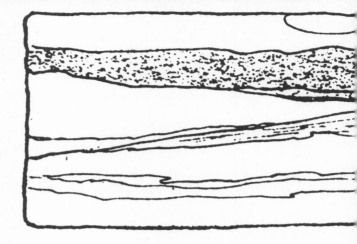

I wanted to write a song that paid tribute to Curley Fletcher and other cowboy minstrels of the early days. I didn't have the foggiest idea how or what I was going to write with the title I had dreamed up, until one day I was reading some of William Wordsworth's poetry and came across a poem called "The Solitary Reaper." As I read and reread this poem, words began coming to me as the "Solitary Reaper" became a "Solitary Cowboy." Where the tune came from, I don't know, but I've changed it a little since I first recorded it in 1987.

"THE SOLITARY REAPER"
A Poem by William Wordsworth

Behold her, single in the field,
Yon solitary Highland Lass!
Reaping and singing by herself;
Stop here, on gently pass!
Alone she cuts and binds the grain,
And sings a melancholy strain;
Oh listen! for the Vale profound
Is overflowing with the sound.

MINSTREL OF THE RANGE
Don Edwards

See him out there on the prairie alone,
A solitary cowboy from out of the past.
Ridin' and singin' all by himself,
Of the old singing cowboys, he may be the last.

With a war bag of songs and a wore-out guitar,
He chases the sundown and sings to the stars.
Listen to him singing his melancholy strain;
He's a wandering minstrel of the range.

No wanderer I've known could ever sing
More welcome songs to a weary herd—
As he sang to the cattle on those dark lonely nights,
His voice softly ringing like his jingle-bobbed spurs.

He'd rather be singing to the cattle at night
An' feel the warmth of a campfire to cold city lights.
He don't really care about fortune and fame;
He's a wandering minstrel of the range.

The range is a-changing into neon and noise,
And folks have lost touch with the land.
They may tap their feet to an old cowboy song,
But mostly they don't understand—

The feeling you get from a campfire's warm glow
As the plaintive notes of his songs softly flow—
Songs about cowboys an' horses an' trains;
He's a disappearing minstrel of the range.

Don Edwards, minstrel of the range, pauses to savor the San Juan mountain range near Chama, New Mexico.

See him out there on the prai - rie a - lone, A sol - i - tar - y

cow - boy from out of the past. Rid - in' and sing - in' all by him -

self, Of the old sing - ing cow - boys, he may be the last. With a

war - bag of songs and a wore - out gui - tar, He chas - es the sun - down and

sings to the stars. Lis - ten to him sing - ing his mel - an - chol - y strain;

He's a wan - der - ing min - strel of _____ the range.

My Heart's Tonight in Texas

(by the Silver Rio Grande)

This song was written around 1900, with words by poet Robert F. Roden and music by Max S. Witt. I've seen some early sheet music of the song, but it has all since passed into public domain. The song has been recorded many times and is still as good a song as it was in 1900.

MY HEART'S TONIGHT IN TEXAS (BY THE SILVER RIO GRANDE)

Lyrics by Robert F. Roden
Music by Max S. Witt
Arrangement and Adaptation by Don Edwards

In the Lone Star State of Texas by the silver Rio Grande
Strolled a couple one fine evening, two sweethearts hand in hand.
'Twas the ranchman's pretty daughter, and the lad she loved so dear.
On the morrow they must part for many a weary year.

Chorus:
My heart's tonight in Texas, though I'm far across the sea,
For the band is playing Dixie, and it's there I long to be.
Dad says some earl I'll marry, but you shall have my hand,
For my heart's tonight in Texas by the silver Rio Grande.

To England she was going to become a lady grand
Where her father hoped some earl or else some count she'd wed.
She left the ranch next morning, though her heart was true to Jack.
Only yesterday a letter came, and it was thus it read:

Chorus

In a stately hall in London stood the Texas lass one night.
The scene was one of splendor, the lights were burning bright.
Before her knelt an earl asking her to take his hand,
But her thoughts were back in Texas by the silver Rio Grande.

Chorus

"I can't say yes," she answered. "Your title I can't take.
There's a lad away in Texas, and they call him Texas Jack.
It is long ago I promised that dear Texas lad to wed.
Only yesterday I wrote, and it's thus the letter said:

Chorus

In the Lone Star State of Tex - as by the sil - ver Ri - o Grande Strolled a

cou - ple one fine eve - ning, two sweet-hearts hand in hand. 'Twas the ranch-er's pret-ty daugh-ter, and the

lad she loved so dear. On the mor-row they must part for man-y a wea-ry

year. My heart's to-night in Tex - as, though I'm far a-cross the sea, For the

band is play-ing Dix - ie, and it's there I long to be. Dad says some earl I'll mar-ry, but

you shall have my hand, For my heart's to-night in Tex - as by the sil - ver Ri - o Grande.

"Meditation"

A Poem by Curley Fletcher

The soft wind sways the whispering grass;
The sun sinks low o'er the western pass
As a coyote mingles his dismal howl
With the sad, sweet notes of a lone hoot owl.

A hawk soars lazily up on high,
A speck of black in a crimson sky.
As a nightingale croons his evening song,
A gray wolf slinks through the shadows long.

The shadows deepen; then the rising moon,
With its silvery radiance all too soon
Dispels the darkness and brings to view
The myriad things of the night anew.

A chuckling porcupine wends his way
To his feeding ground, ere the break of day;
A mighty stag comes browsing on
With a graceful doe and a timid fawn.

Then a sadness grips you like a pall
In the silvery gloom where the shadows fall;
Then you wonder why you feel depressed;
Though you are alone, you have not guessed.

'Tis because you are a poacher there—
Unclean, where nature's breast lies bare.
And you would this place so sweet, so grand,
Might remain untarnished by human hand.

But e'en this spot shall see the day
When it will fall to easy prey
Of lust and greed, and in the place
Where yon pine sways in supple grace

An ax-scarred stump will stand instead,
Bowing in shame its branchless head,
And down the rivers will flow the spoils,
All hopeless victims to human toils.

The drumming grouse will seek in vain
For the cozy coverts to nest again.
The quaking aspens will tremble ashamed
For the towering forests so torn and maimed.

The work of aeons will fall away
To the reaper's stroke in a single day;
Though the future ages may never mend
The scars of greed till the end of end.

The Old Cow Man

THE OLD COW MAN

Lyrics by Charles "Badger" Clark
Music by Don Edwards

I rode across a valley range I hadn't seen for years;
The trail was all so spoilt and strange, it nearly fetched the tears.
I had to let ten fences down, the fussy lanes ran wrong,
And each new line would make me frown and hum a mournful song.

Oh, ooh, ooh, ooh . . . . . .
Hear 'em stretchin' of the wire!
The urban brand is on the land,
So I reckon I'll retire
While progress toots its greedy horn
And makes its motor buzz;
I thank the Lord I wasn't born
No later than I was.

'Twas good to live when all the sod without no fence nor fuss
Belonged in pardnership to God, Mother Nature, and to us;
With skyline bounds from east to west and room to go and come,
I loved my fellow man the best when he was scattered some.

Oh, ooh, ooh, ooh . . . . . .
Closer and closer cramps the wire.
There's hardly play to back away
And call a man a liar;
Their house has locks on every door,
Their land is in a crate.
These ain't the plains of God no more
They're only real estate.

When my old soul hunts range and rest beyond the last divide,
Just plant me in some stretch of West that's sunny, lone, and wide;
Let cattle rub my tombstone down and coyotes mourn their kin;
Let horses paw and tromp the moun', but don't you fence it in!

Oh, oooh, oooh, oooh . . . . . .
Far and farther flings the wire;
To crowd and pinch another inch
Is all their heart's desire.
The world is overstocked with men,
And some will see the day
When each must keep his little pen,
But I'll be far away.

While progress toots its greedy horn
And makes its motor buzz,
I thank the Lord I wasn't born
No later than I was.

Like most of Charles "Badger" Clark's poetry, "The Old Cow Man" has that wonderful melodic flow that lends itself to music. This poem has no doubt been set to music many times since Badger wrote it during his cowboy days in Arizona. In fact, it's just as common to hear someone refer to his poetry as songs just as often as they refer to them as poems. I don't believe a person can call himself a cowboy singer without knowing a few Badger Clark songs. It would be like calling yourself a cowboy and not knowing how to ride a horse.

I've always heard stories of how someone had this dream or some kind of vision where a whole song came to them in their sleep, "It just wrote itself," they said. I wasn't much for believing this sort of thing could happen until it happened to me. One night a while back, I had gone to bed, and for whatever reason I couldn't get to sleep. Well, my mind goes to wandering, and I start reciting this poem to myself. I guess I drifted off to sleep 'cause the next thing I remember is this tune from who-knows-where pops into my head. I get out of bed and get my guitar and start singing this song into my recording machine. I had tried to set this poem to music on many occasions, but nothing ever fit until then. It all just sort of flowed together all at once. This has never happened to me before or since.

I play this song in the key of C but capoed at the fourth fret in G position.

I rode a-cross a val-ley range __ I had-n't seen for years; __ The

trail was all so spoilt and strange, __ it near - ly fetched the tears. __ I

had to let __ ten fenc-es down, __ the fus-sy lanes __ ran wrong, And

each new line __ would make me frown __ and hum a mourn-ful song. __

Oh, ooh, ooh, ooh __ Hear 'em stretch-in' of the wire! __ The

ur-ban brand is on the land, __ So I reck-on I'll __ re-tire __

While prog-ress toots its greed-y horn And makes its mo-tor buzz; __ I

thank the Lord __ I was-n't born __ No la-ter than I was.

Patonio, Pride of the Plains

Most of my singing cowboy friends lament at some time or another of being born too late to have partaken in song collecting firsthand. I was born during the first half of the twentieth century, and my first introduction to cowboy songs was from phonograph records. I first heard this song from a recording of Hawkshaw Hawkins from WWVA in Wheeling, West Virginia, while still a youngster living back East. Hawkshaw was a country singer who also sang cowboy songs as so many did back then. I later found the song in Margaret Larkin's book *Singing Cowboy*.

I've never played anywhere that this song hasn't been requested. I have also never seen it spelled the same way twice. There's Patonio, Platonio, Plantonio—no matter how it's spelled, it's a great song.

PATONIO, PRIDE OF THE PLAINS

Traditional

I'll tell you a story that will thrill you, I know,
Of a horse I once owned in New Mexico.
You will gaze at his picture with wondering eyes
And then at the arrow that hangs by its side.

He was swift as an antelope and black as a crow
With a star on his forehead as white as the snow.
His arched neck was covered with a dark flowing mane,
And I called him Patonio, the pride of the plains.

The country was new, and the settlers was scarce.
The Indians on the warpath were savage and fierce.
Though the scouts were sent out everyday from the fort,
Yet they never came back, so we knew they were lost.

One day the captain says, "Someone must go
Across the dark borders of New Mexico."
A dozen young fellows straightaway answered, "Here!"
But the captain spied me: I was standing right near.

Patonio was by me, his nose in my hand.
Said the captain, "Your horse is the best in the land.
You're good for the ride; you're the lightest man here;
On the back of that mustang, you have nothing to fear."

Then proud of my pony, I answered, "You know
Patonio and I are both willing to go.
For speed and endurance I'll trust in my black."
Then they all shook my hand, and I mounted his back.

Turned down the dark pathway, turned his head to the right,
The black struck a trot, and he kept it all night.
When far back behind me, I hear a shrill wail;
I knew that the Indians were hot on my trail.

I'll tell you a sto-ry that will thrill you, I know, Of a horse I once owned in New Mex-i-co. You will gaze at his pic-ture with won-der-ing eyes And then at the ar-row that hangs by its side.

I jingled the bells at the end of his rein,
Spoke his name softly, and stroked his dark mane.
Patonio answered with a nod of his head;
His dark body lengthened as faster we sped.

We were leaving the Indians, the story was plain.
The arrows fell 'round us like torrents of rain.
Patonio, he stumbled—I knew he was hurt—
But still he raced onward and into the fort.

I delivered the message then tried to dismount,
But the pain in my foot was so bad I could not.
The arrow you see hanging there on the wall
Had passed through my foot, saddle, stirrup, and all.

With good care and patience, Pat and I were soon well.
Of his death many years later, I will not try to tell.
Of all the fine horses I've rode o'er the range,
There was none like Patonio, the pride of the plains.

The Pecos River Queen

Not far from Langtry, Texas, is the Comstock Railroad trestle, which was said to have been the highest in the West. The famous Judge Roy Bean told Jack Thorp about how a pretty Texas cowgirl by the name of Patty Moorhead rode her horse across the trestle.

Jack wrote the song from the story Bean had told him and made Patty Moorhead "The Pecos River Queen." He took liberty to introduce a cowpuncher lover whom Patty said she would marry if he would follow her across the trestle a-horseback. He was afraid to follow her, so she remained unwed.

Thorp admired the frontier women and wrote many anecdotes about them. I also believe that women played just as big a part in shaping the history of the American West as the men did.

THE PECOS RIVER QUEEN

N. Howard "Jack" Thorp

Where the Pecos River winds and turns in its journey to the sea,
From its white wall of sand and rock striving ever to be free,
Near the highest railroad bridge that all these modern times have seen,
Dwells fair young Patty Moorhead, the Pecos River Queen.

She's known by all the cowboys on the Pecos River wide;
They know full well that she can shoot, that she can rope and ride;
She goes to every roundup, every cow-work without fail,
Lookin' out for all her cattle, branded "walkin' hog on rail."

She made her start in cattle, yes, she made it with her rope;
Can tie down any maverick 'fore it can strike a lope;
She can rope and tie and brand it as quick as any man;
She's voted by all the cowboys an A-1 top cowhand.

Across the Comstock Railroad bridge, the highest in the West,
Patty rode her horse one day, a lover's heart to test;
For he told her he would gladly risk all dangers for her sake,
But the puncher wouldn't follow, so she's still without a mate.

Where the Pecos River winds and turns in its journey to the sea,
From its white walls of sand and rock striving ever to be free,
Near the highest railroad bridge that all these modern times have seen,
Dwells fair young Patty Moorhead, the Pecos River Queen.

At the Caravan of Dreams in Fort Worth, Texas, Tish Hinojosa and Don put heart and soul into their duet.

Where the Pe - cos Riv - er winds and turns in its jour - ney to the sea, From its

white wall of sand and rock striv - ing ev - er to be free, Near the

high - est rail - road bridge that all these mod - ern times have seen, Dwells

fair young Pat - ty Moor - head, she's the Pe - cos Riv - er Queen.

A Philosophical Cowboy

I found this song in Austin and Alta Fife's book *Cowboy and Western Songs*. It was originally a freighting song, but I liked this cowboy version, so I just put some music to it and thought it made a pretty good song. The cowboy philosophy here can pertain to any walk of life.

A PHILOSOPHICAL COWBOY

Traditional
Music by Don Edwards

On the Double Circle range where the grass grows green,
The cattle get wild and the broncos get mean;
And the calves get bigger as the days go by,
So we got to keep a-rimmin', boys, it's root hog or die.

If you ride them out of horses, you've got to keep them shod;
If you can't shoe them standing, then lay them on the sod.
You can tack the iron on them if you've a mind to try;
So get busy, boys, for it's root hog or die.

In the morning after breakfast about daylight,
Throw your saddle on a horse and pull your cinches tight;
Your bronc may jump crooked or he may jump high,
But we all got to ride them, boys, it's root hog or die.

Oh, the hills are rough and rocky, but we got to make the drive;
When you start a bunch of cattle, you better come alive.
If you ever get a maverick, you must get him on the fly,
So you better take to them, boys, it's root hog or die.

When the long day is over, you'll be glad to see the chief
With a pot of black coffee and another full of beef,
And some sourdough biscuits to take the place of pie.
When he hollers, "Come and get it," it's root hog or die.

In the middle of the night, it is sometimes awful hard
To leave your warm blankets when you're called on guard,
And you pass the weary moments while the stars are in the sky
Humming to the cattle, boys, it's root hog or die.

Sometimes it's dreadful stormy, and sometimes it's pretty clean,
You may work a month or you might work a year.
But you can make a winning if you'll come alive and try,
For the whole world over, boys, it's root hog or die.

On the Dou – ble Cir – cle range _ where the grass grows green, The cat – tle _ get wild and the bron – cos _ get mean; And the calves get big – ger as _ the _ days _ go by, So we got to keep _ a – rim – min', boys, it's root hog or die. _

On location at old Tucson, Don and friends film the TNN special "Music of the Wild West."

Poor Lonesome Cowboy

To quote Carl Sandburg in *The American Songbag* on "Poor Lonesome Cowboy": "It is a species of cowboy blues, the range riders moan." It should be sung "sad, and worse than sad."

I've been singing country folk-style blues for as long as I've sung cowboy songs. Back when I was growing up, there were still very few categories for musical styles. In the nineteenth century, there were none; there was just music—music of many styles and cultures—all merging together. There was no definition of blues as a genre then, but the music was there. African influences mixing with Celtic styles were common among cowboys, especially in Texas where, for the most part, there were no prejudices as to race, religion, etc. As long as you could do the job, that was all that mattered.

The same was true for the music. What inspired Jack Thorp to quit his job cowboying on the Bar W and take a year off to travel the West in search of cowboy songs was when he rode into a camp of mostly black cowboys and heard singing and playing that was different from anything he had ever heard before. Like Thorp, I have always been inspired and motivated by the mixing and blending of musical culture and the fascinating similarities of homemade music.

The country folk-style blues and traditional cowboy songs were very similar because they were generally the "make 'em up as you go along" kind of songs.

The early blues singers and songsters played the barrel houses, just one man, a guitar or banjo, singing his made-up songs for the dancers for three or four hours at a time without stopping for a break. It's ironic that my own career was a direct parallel, carrying on the same tradition for fifteen years at the White Elephant Saloon in Fort Worth, Texas.

Just as the songster sang for the dancers in the rural South, the cowboy sang his made-up songs to the cattle on the vast open rangeland of the West.

POOR LONESOME COWBOY

Traditional
Arrangement and Adaptation by Don Edwards

Oh, sunrise is a comin'
And a comin' mighty soon;
Git up and roll, little dogies,
And say good mornin' to the moon.

I ain't got no father,
I ain't got no father,
I ain't got no father
To buy the clothes I wear.

Chorus:
I'm a poor lonesome cowboy,
I'm a poor lonesome cowboy,
Oh, I'm weary and loneful
And a long ways from home.

I ain't got no mother,
I ain't got no mother,
I ain't got no mother
To mend the clothes I wear.

Chorus

I ain't got no brother,
I ain't got no brother,
I ain't got no brother
To ride the range with me.

Chorus

I ain't got no sweetheart,
I ain't got no sweetheart,
I ain't got no sweetheart
To sit and talk with me.

Chorus

The Railroad Corral

This song describes the last days of a cattle drive. The original title was simply "Cowboy Song" and it was written by Joseph Mills Hanson of Yankton, South Dakota, in 1904. It's believed that the song was based on the Scottish ballad "Bonnie Dundee." The title was changed to "The Railroad Corral" and passed into oral folk song tradition a mere six years after it was written.

The cowboy's relation with railroads was bittersweet. He was glad there were railroads to take his cattle to market. But, on the other hand, he hated them because they eventually brought civilization to his beloved West. Still, the cowboy loved to sing railroad songs, especially ones about head-on collisions, and he wasn't immune to the romance of the rails that was synonymous with going places and moving on.

THE RAILROAD CORRAL

Joseph Mills Hanson

We're up in the mornin' at the breakin' of day—
The chuck wagon's busy; the flapjacks' in play.
The herd is astir over hillside and vale,
And the night riders roundin' 'em onto the trail.

Come take up your cinches and shake out your reins.
Wake your old bronco and break for the plains.
Come roust out your steers from the long chaparral,
For the outfit is off to the railroad corral.

The sun circles upward; the steers as they plod
Are poundin' to powder the hot prairie sod.
And it seems, as the dust makes you dizzy and sick,
That we'll never reach noon and the cool shady crik.

Tie up your kerchief and ply up your nag;
Come dry up your grumbles and try not to lag.
Come drive out your steers from the long chaparral,
For we're far on the trail to the railroad corral.

The afternoon shadows are startin' to lean
When the chuck wagon sticks in a marshy ravine.
The herd scatters farther than vision can look.
You can bet all true punchers will help out the cook.

Come shake out your rawhide and shake it out fair,
Come break your old bronco to take in his share.
Come roust out your steers from the long chaparral,
For it's all in the drive to the railroad corral.

The longest of days must reach evenin' at last.
The hills are all climbed, and the creeks are all past.
The tired herd droops in the yellowin' light.
Let 'em rest if they will, for the railroad's in sight.

So flap up your holster and snap up your belt,
And strap up your saddle whose lap you have felt.
Say good-bye to the steers from the long chaparral,
For there's a town that's a trunk by the railroad corral.

G   C   G

We're up in the morn – in' at the break – in' of day — The

C   G

chuck wag – on's bus – y; the flap – jacks' in play.   The

Em   Bm

herd is a – stir o – ver hill – side and vale,   And the

G   C   G   C   G

night rid – ers round – in' 'em on – to the trail. _____

Katharine Field – 35.

Rambling Cowboy

There are many variations of this song both in lyrics and melodies. I believe the melody that I have given here is a combination of "Rising Sun Blues" and a British ballad, "Lord Barnard."

RAMBLING COWBOY

Traditional
Arrangement and Adaptation by Don Edwards

I am a rambling cowboy just off the stormy plains;
If there ever was a hell on earth, it was holding my bridle reins.

My papa always taught me well and gave me good advice,
But my mind was on rambling, and we could not agree.

I left the state of Texas; Arizona I was bound.
I landed in Tombstone City and viewed the place all around.

Money and work were plentiful, and the cowboys they were kind,
But the only thought in my heart was the girl I left behind.

One day as I was riding across the public square,
The mail coach had just arrived, and I met the driver there.

He handed down a letter that I might understand
That girl I left in Texas had married another man.

I turned myself all around, not knowing what to do,
And as I read that letter down, it proved the words were true.

Hard work I have laid aside, and rambling I resigned;
I'll ramble all this wide world o'er for the gal I thought was mine.

I rode back to the cattle range, corn dodger was my bread;
The dearest one to me is gone; oh, I wish that I was dead.

There is a girl in Baxter Springs, they call her Rising Sun;
She's broke the heart of many a poor boy, and my poor heart is one.

So when you meet a pretty girl, and she fills your heart with joy,
Just marry her while you can; take heed, you rambling cowboys.

Come all you reckless rambling boys who have listened to my song,
If it hasn't done you any good, it hasn't done you any wrong.

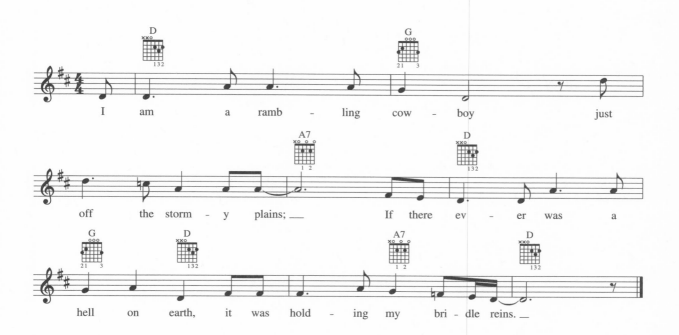

I am a ramb - ling cow - boy just
off the storm - y plains; ___ If there ev - er was a
hell on earth, it was hold - ing my bri - dle reins. ___

The Rancher's Song

I took the old rendition of "The Farmer's Song" and changed it into "The Rancher's Song." Some say it came out of the 1860s, but its earliest origins were most likely from sixteenth-century England. "The Farmer's Song" has appeared in many collections, including Carl Sandburg's *American Songbag*. The song is also found under the title "The Farmer Feeds Us All." The most recent recording of this song that I have found is by Ry Cooder.

I rewrote the song to bring about more awareness of the plight of the rancher. Like the farmer, he's getting a bad rap from the government as well as all those pseudo-environmentalists. But unlike the farmer, he doesn't receive any subsidies for what he doesn't raise.

Even though I'm a rancher of sorts myself, I'm not really qualified to get into any long-winded details on the matter. That's better left up to the ranchers who do it full time. I can probably do a better job just passing the word on through my songs.

THE RANCHER'S SONG

Traditional
Arrangement and Adaptation by Don Edwards

The cowboy's work is never done,
He works hard from sun to sun;
The cow man is the man who feeds us all.
Now people jump and shout;
They say, "We want the rancher out!"
They forget that it's the rancher feeds them all.

The rancher is the man;
The rancher is the man;
He lives on credit till the fall.
They don't want him raisin' cattle;
They want the land for raisin' hell!
The rancher is the man who feeds them all.

The lawyer hangs around
While the butcher cuts a pound;
The rancher is the man who feeds them all.
The preacher and the cook,
They go strolling by the brook
While the rancher is the man who feeds them all.

The rancher is the man;
The rancher is the man;
He lives on credit till the fall.
But with the taxes so damn high,
It's a wonder he don't die.
The tax man's the man who gets it all.

Now the rancher comes to town
With his wagons broken down;
The rancher is the man who feeds us all.
The banker says he's broke
'Cause the country's up in smoke;
Still the rancher is the man who feeds them all.

The rancher is the man;
The rancher is the man;
He lives on credit till the fall.
With the interest that he pays
Soon takes his money all away,
And the mortgage man's the man who gets it all.

Now the government wants his land,
But they just don't understand—
The rancher is the man who feeds them all.
It would put them to the test
If the rancher took a rest.
The rancher is the man who feeds them all.

The rancher is the man;
The rancher is the man;
He lives on credit till the fall.
Then they take him by the hand,
And they lead him off his land.
The rancher is the man who feeds them all,
And Uncle Sam's the man who gets it all.

The cow-boy's work is nev-er done, ___ He works hard from sun to sun; ___ The

cow man is the man who feeds us all. ___ Now peo-ple jump and shout; ___ They say, "We

want the ranch-er out!" They for-get that it's the ranch-er feeds them all. ___

___ The ranch-er is the man; ___ The ranch-er is the man; ___ He

lives on cred-it till the fall. ___ They don't want him rais-in' cat-tle; ___ they want the

land ___ for rais-in' hell! ___ The ranch-er is the man ___ who feeds them all. ___

Red River Valley

This became a cowboy song when someone moved its location to the Red River that borders Texas and Oklahoma, and added the word cowboy to the lyrics. The song was thought to have started in the Mohawk Valley of New York, then moved to the logging camps of Manitoba, Canada, and finally to the Southwest.

There are literally hundreds of recordings of this song. I recorded it on my *Happy Cowboy* album in 1980. This is another great sing-along campfire-type song that should be in everybody's repertoire. There's not a cowboy singer alive who doesn't know this one.

RED RIVER VALLEY
Traditional

From this valley they say you are going;
I will miss your bright eyes and sweet smile.
For they say you are taking the sunshine
That has brightened our pathway awhile.

Chorus:
Come and sit by my side if you love me;
Do not hasten to bid me adieu.
Just remember the Red River Valley
And the cowboy who loved you so true.

I've been waiting a long time, my darling,
For the sweet words you never would say.
Now all of my fond hopes have vanished,
For they say you are going away.

Chorus

Oh, there could never be such a longing
In the heart of a poor cowboy's breast
That now dwells in the heart you are breaking,
As I wait in my home in the West.

Chorus

The coyotes will howl all around me
While so sadly I strum my guitar,
While I pour out the love I must vanquish
Into the mirage of a star.

Chorus

Do you think of the valley you're leaving,
Oh, how lonely and dreary it will be?
Do you think of the kind heart you're breaking
And the pain you are causing to me?

Chorus

Don cohosts the grand reopening of the Plaza Theater in El Paso, Texas, with Ana-Alicia.

D A7 D

From this val – ley they say you are go – ing; ___ I will

A7 D D7

miss your bright eyes and sweet smile. _ For they say you are tak – ing the sun –

G A7 D

shine ___ That has bright – ened our path – way a – while.

Katherine Field – 55.

The Ridge-Running Roan

One of my favorite Curley Fletcher poems is "The Ridge-Running Roan." It always gets overshadowed by the famous roan of another color. Hardly anyone sings this anymore, and I think it's about time it made a comeback at the Cowboy Gatherings or wherever else pickers and singers congregate to recite poetry and swap songs.

One of the earliest recordings of this song was by Glen Rice and his Beverly Hillbillies. The Beverly Hillbillies were one of the first groups to sing western harmony later made famous by the Sons of the Pioneers. The group had several later-to-be-famous members, including Stuart Hamblin, Lloyd Perryman, and Elton Britt. There have been numerous other recordings of this song, but no matter who sings it, it's still one of the best horse songs ever written.

THE RIDGE-RUNNING ROAN

Curley Fletcher

I was out in the badlands a rangin' alone
When I hears of a cayuse—the ridge-runnin' roan.
He was fleet as a deer and tough as a mule,
Pretty as a picture, and nobody's fool.

High-headed and leggy, he was just built for speed;
The cowboy that roped him could own that there steed.
I figured the reason this bronc was still free:
He never had crossed a mustanger like me.

I goes right to work, and I gets me a pair
Of the best saddle horses that ever wore hair.
I'd hunt up that mustang and camp on his trail;
When he hit for the ridges, he was packin' the mail.

He was tough as a boot and as wise as a fox;
He kept on the ridges and a-dodgin' the rocks.
I'd trail him till dark, and at dawn I'd begin,
Till I got pretty weak and my horses got thin.

I followed those tracks till I got stiff and sore;
But he stayed right in front where he kept makin' more.
He don't get much water and no time to graze,
While I camped on his trail for seventeen days.

Then he got awful gaunt, he was wearin' out fast,
Till he looked like a ridge-runnin' ghost at the last.
He was placin' his feet like he was walkin' on tacks,
Till I saw he was leavin' fresh blood in his tracks.

I started to crowd him and turned him around;
He quit the rough ridges and hunted soft ground.
I shook out a loop when we got to a flat;
I threw that riata and it fit like my hat.

He sure gave up quick when I jerked out the slack,
Then I noticed some ole saddle marks on his back.
I had done myself proud, and I felt like a champ
When I got him all haltered and headed for camp.

Well, I got him at home and into the corral;
I fed him some hay and some oats for a spell.
When he got fat and strong, I gave him the news;
I hog-tied him down, and I nailed on some shoes.

I threw on my saddle and cinched it right down;
Then I crawled his old carcass, I was headed for town.
I drug out my quirt 'cause to me he looked tame
Like a twenty-two pistol on a forty-five frame.

He let out a bawl, and he went from that spot,
Like the ground where he stood had sudden got hot.
He was mad as a hornet, and I guess he saw red,
'Cause he was handy a-foot, and his feet wasn't lead.

I was doin' my best and was just gettin' by,
But he's doin' better with blood in his eye.
I thought I was up on the hurricane deck
Of an earthquake and a cyclone, a havin' a wreck.

He was duckin' and dodgin' and a-walkin' the dog;
He had me so dizzy, I was lost in the fog.
He was bawlin' and gruntin', a-humpin' the hump;
He turned wrong side out with every new jump.

With a gyratin' jump, he goes over the gate,
And I grabbed for the horn, but I was too late.
He hit with a jar that 'most shed his hair;
It busted me loose, and I quit him right there.

I was out in the bad-lands a rang-in' a-lone When I hears of a cay-use — the ridge-run-nin' roan. He was fleet as a deer and tough as a mule, Pret-ty as a pic-ture, and no-bod-y's fool, High-head-ed and leg-gy, he was just built for speed; The cow-boy that roped him could own that there steed. I fig-ured the rea-son this bronc was still free: He nev-er had crossed a mus-tang-er like me.

Now, at ridin' bad horses, I'm no crippled squaw;
But he showed me some tricks that I never saw.
He busted me up, and I'm still stiff and lame,
That ridge-runnin' outlaw will never be tame.

The last time I saw him, he was a crossin' a bridge;
He was high-tailin' back to his favorite ridge.
I've borrowed an outfit, as I've none of my own;
My riggin' ran off with that ridge-runnin' roan.

Ridin'

This was Charles "Badger" Clark's first published poem. Its original title was "In Arizony" and appeared in the August 1906 issue of *Pacific Monthly* magazine. In 1915, Clark published a book of poems called *Sun and Saddle Leather* and changed the title of the poem to "Ridin'."

The poem has been set to music many times over the years but this is my own version I've given here. I also use the song with Waddie Mitchell's poem "Commutin'." Both the song and the poem tell of the cowboy's love of being a-horseback.

RIDIN'

Lyrics by Charles "Badger" Clark
Music by Don Edwards

There is some that like the city
Grass that's curried smooth and green,
Theayters and stranglin' collars,
Wagons run by gasoline.
But for me it's hawse and saddle
Every day without a change,
And a desert sun a-blazin'
On a hundred miles of range.
Just a-ridin', a-ridin'—
Desert ripplin' in the sun,
Mountains blue along the skyline—
I don't envy anyone when I'm ridin'.

When my feet is in the stirrups
And my hawse is on the bust,
With his hoofs a-flashin' lightnin'
From a cloud of golden dust,
And the bawlin' of the cattle
Is a-comin' down the wind,
Then a finer life than ridin'
Would be mighty hard to find.
Just a-ridin', a-ridin',
Splittin' long cracks through the air,
Stirrin' up a baby cyclone,
Rippin' up the prickly pear as I'm ridin'.

I don't need no art exhibits
When the sunset does her best
Paintin' everlastin' glory
On the mountains to the west.
And your opery looks so foolish
When the nightbird starts his tune,
And the desert's silver-mounted
By the touches of the moon.
Just a-ridin', a-ridin'—
Who kin envy kings and czars
When the coyotes down the valley
Are a-singin' to the stars, if he's ridin'?

When my earthly trail is ended
And my final bacon curled
And the last great roundup's finished
At the Home Ranch of the world,
I don't want no harps nor halos,
Robes nor other dressed-up things.
Let me ride the starry ranges
On a pinto hawse with wings!
Just a-ridin', a-ridin'—
Nothin' I'd like half so well
As a-roundin' up the sinners
That have wandered out of hell, and a-ridin'.

D Em

There is some that like the ci-ty Grass that's cur-ried sooth and green, The-

A7 D

ay-ters and strang-lin' col-lars, Wa-gons run by gas-o-line. But for

D Em

me it's hawse and sad-dle Ev-'ry day with-out a change, And the

A7 D

des-ert sun a-blaz-in' On a hun-dred miles of range. Just a-

G A7 D Bm

rid-in', a-rid-in', — Des-ert rip-plin' in the sun. Moun-tains

G Em A7 D

blue a-long the sky-line — I don't en-vy an-y-one when I'm rid-in'. ___

Rounded Up in Glory

This song is a true cowboy hymn. I have no idea who wrote it, but the last recorded version that I'm aware of was by Tex Ritter. The old-time cowboys sang more hymns than any other kind of song. Most of the old night-herding songs were hymns, or at least the tunes were used and set to their homemade lyrics.

The cowboy wasn't part of organized religion, and he wasn't much for church-goin'. According to Charles "Badger" Clark in his poem "A Cowboy's Prayer," the cowboy "loved creation better as it stood that day God finished it so long ago and looked upon His work and called it good." On the other hand, one must realize the cowboy wasn't an irreligious or godless individual either. He was a man with a strong moral code and a casual philosophy that resulted from his closeness with nature. Because of his environment, his knowledge of right and wrong was crystal clear. God was good; the devil was bad. The passing from life to death was always west of West and beyond the Great Divide.

"A COWBOY'S PRAYER"

A Poem by Charles "Badger" Clark

Oh Lord, I've never lived where churches grow.
I love creation better as it stood
That day you finished it so long ago.
And looked upon your work and called it good.

I know that others see you in the light
That's sifted down through tinted windowpanes,
And yet I seem to feel you near tonight
In this dim, quiet starlight on the plains.

I thank you, Lord, that I am placed so well
That you have made my freedom so complete;
That I'm no slave of whistle, clock, or bell,
Nor weak-eyed prisoner of wall and street.

Just let me live my life as I've begun
And give me work that's open to the sky;
Make me a pardner of the wind and sun,
And I won't ask for a life that's soft or high.

Let me be easy on the man that's down;
Let me be square and generous with all.
I'm careless sometimes, Lord, when I'm in town,
But never let 'em say I'm mean or small!

Make me as big and open as the plains,
As honest as this horse between my knees,
Clean as the wind that blows behind the rains,
Free as the hawk that circles down the breeze!

Forgive me, Lord, if sometimes I forget.
You know about the reasons that are hid.
You understand the things that gall and fret;
You know me better than my mother did.

Just keep an eye on all that's done and said,
And right me, sometimes, when I turn aside,
And guide me on that long, dim trail ahead
That stretches upward toward the Great Divide.

ROUNDED UP IN GLORY

Traditional
Arrangement and Adaptation by Don Edwards

I've been thinkin' today,
As my thoughts began to stray,
Of your memory to me worth more than gold.
As you ride across the plain
'Mid the sunshine and the rain,
You'll be rounded up in glory bye and bye.

C h o r u s :
You will be rounded up in glory bye and bye.
You will be rounded up in glory bye and bye.
When the millin' time is o'er,
And you will stampede no more,
When He rounds you up within the Master's fold.

As you ride across the plain
With the cowboys that have fame,
And the storms and the lightning flash by,
We shall meet to part no more,
When He rounds us up in glory bye and bye.

May we lift our voices high
To that sweet bye and bye,
And be known by the brand of the Lord;
For His property we are,
And He will know us from afar
When He rounds us up in glory bye and bye.

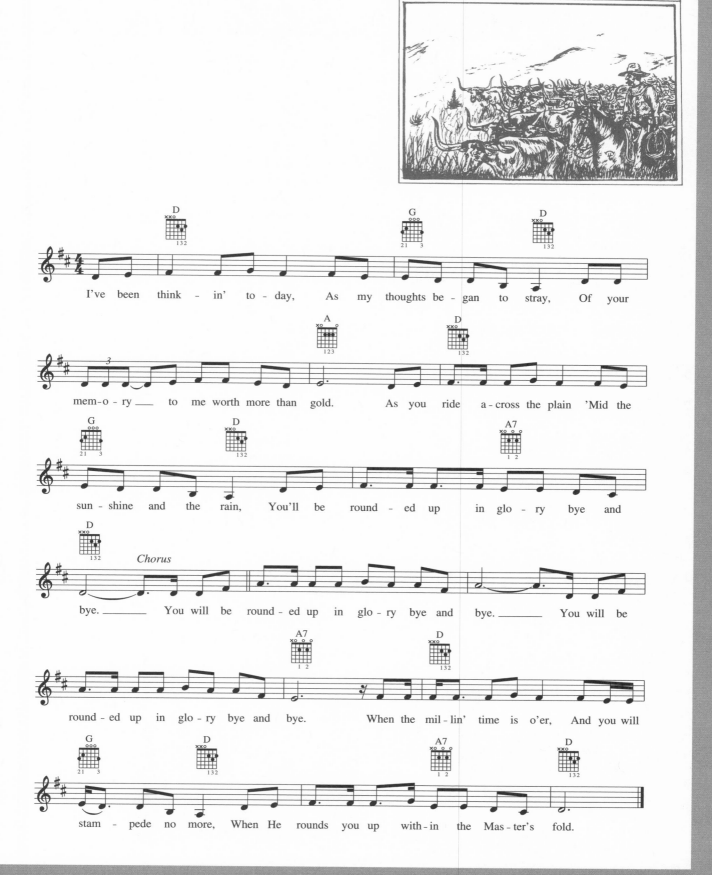

I've been think-in' to-day, As my thoughts be-gan to stray, Of your

mem-o-ry ___ to me worth more than gold. As you ride a-cross the plain 'Mid the

sun-shine and the rain, You'll be round-ed up in glo-ry bye and

Chorus

bye. _____ You will be round-ed up in glo-ry bye and bye. _____ You will be

round-ed up in glo-ry bye and bye. When the mil-in' time is o'er, And you will

stam-pede no more, When He rounds you up with-in the Mas-ter's fold.

Run Along, Little Dogies

This is a variation of "Whoopie-Ti-Yi-Yo," the popular old cowboy song whose origins were traced back to Ireland and the song "The Old Man's Lament," a lullaby written around 1660. The songs have a unique and interesting parallel—motherless calves and a fatherless child. I had originally showed that parallel in my first anthology, *Songs of the Cowboy*. This song has a few different stanzas, but the melody remains the same.

RUN ALONG, LITTLE DOGIES

Traditional
Arrangement and Adaptation by Don Edwards

As I was a ridin' one morning for pleasure,
I spied a cowpuncher a-lopin' along;
His hat was throwed back and his spurs were a-jinglin',
And as he drew near, he was singing this song.

Hush-ie-ci-olo, little baby, lie easy,
Who's your real daddy may never be known;
Oh, it's weeping and wailing and rocking the cradle
And tending a baby that's none of my own.

When spring comes along, we round up the dogies;
We mark 'em and brand 'em and bob off their tails;
Round up the horses, load up the chuck wagon;
And throw them dogies out on that long trail.

Singin' hoop-pi-o-hoop, run along, little dogies,
You know that Montana will be your new home;
Oh, it's whoopin' and cussin' and drivin' them dogies;
It's our misfortune we ever did roam.

Oh, it's worse in the night just after the roundup
When the dogies are grazing from the herd all around;
You have no idea the trouble they give us
To the boys who are holding them on the bed ground.

Singin' hush-ie-ci-olo, little dogies, lie easy;
It's your misfortune and none of my own.
Stretch away out on that big open ground;
You know that Montana will be your new home.

Early in the morning, we throw off the bed ground,
Aiming to graze them an hour or two.
When they are full, you think you can drive them
Out on the trail, but be damned if you do.

Now some think we go up the cow trail for pleasure,
But that's where they get it most awfully wrong;
If it hadn't a-been for them troublesome dogies,
I'd have no reason for singing this song.

Whoopie-ti-yi-yo, run along, little dogies;
It's your misfortune and none of my own.
Whoopie-ti-yi-yo, run along, little dogies;
You know that Montana will be your new home.

Saddle Tramp

This is one of my favorite Curley Fletcher poems. The melody is pretty much like I've always heard it, which wasn't too often. This is another song that I strongly relate to. Saddle tramps were not too well liked among ranchers because they never stayed in one place long enough to become dependable hands. But to a wide-eyed, impressionable kid, they were romantic as all get-out. There's good and bad in all of us, and a saddle tramp was no different. Except in the case of the old saying, "You can't judge a book by its cover," you could sure tell a man by his outfit as well as the horse he was riding.

As I said before, professional saddle tramps were not liked in the range country, but there's hardly a cowboy who hasn't been out of a job during certain times who hasn't rode the "chuck-line" while hunting up a new job. As far as the song is concerned, I just hope you'll enjoy singing and playing it as much as I do.

With his horse saddled and his guitar packed, Don heads for the mountains and some high-country singing.

SADDLE TRAMP
Curley Fletcher

I'm known to some as a saddle bum, and ever since the day
I quit the strife of the cowboy life to travel, sing, and play—
A saddle tramp from ranch to camp, traveling near and far,
A horseback bum to sing and strum on my Mexican guitar.

I used to work, but now I shirk, and I never more will hire
To mark an ear, to turn a steer, nor tend a branding fire.
The pie and cake is mine to take the best of everything;
I'll lay my head on the softest bed, play my old guitar, and sing.

Well, here or there or anywhere that I may choose to roam,
Me they'll feed, and my saddle steed will always find a home.
I'll tell you that my horse is fat, and I want you to know
It's mighty fine to ride grub line, and I'm welcome where I go.

I'll stay awhile to sing and smile, but when there comes a rift;
When things get cool, I ain't no fool; I fork my bronc and drift.
I'll ramble down to a little town when winter comes along,
To sweet Lolita, my senorita, and sing for her my song.

When white snow flies from wintery skies and mantles hill and plain,
I'm coming back to that little shack and love you, dear, again.
Sweet Lolita, my senorita, again I've come to you;
So don't you grieve until I leave, while here I will be true.

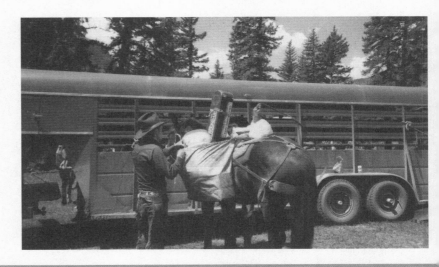

E   A

I'm known to some as a sad-dle bum, and ev - er since the day —

B7

I quit the strife of cow - boy life to trav - el, sing, and

E

play — A sad - dle tramp from ranch to camp, —

A   B7

trav - el - ing near and far, A horse - back bum to

E

sing and strum — on my Mex - i - can — gui - tar.

Sam Bass

Ever since it was first published in 1908 by Jack Thorp, "Sam Bass" has always been a favorite among cowboy singers and folksingers alike. Austin and Alta Fife had discovered an earlier printed text, dated 1906. The song was probably written shortly after Sam's death on July 21, 1878. Thorp said he first heard it at a dance hall in Sidney, Nebraska, in 1888.

The tune I give here is somewhat like Thorp's original tune that came from a frontier ballad, "The Range of the Buffalo," that preceded the Civil War. There are a few variations in my version, but it's still different than any I've heard in recent years.

SAM BASS

Traditional
Arrangement and Adaptation by Don Edwards

Sam Bass was born in Indiana—it was his native home—
And at the age of seventeen, young Sam begun to roam;
He first came out to Texas, a cowboy for to be;
A kinder hearted fellow you hardly ever see.

He used to deal in race stock, one called the Denton mare;
He ran her in scrub races and took her to the fair.
She always won the money wherever she might be;
Sam always drank good whiskey and spent his money free.

Young Sam left the Collins ranch in the merry month of May
With a herd of Texas cattle for the Black Hills far away;
Sold out in Custer City and then went on a spree;
A harder set of cowboys you seldom ever see.

On their way back to Texas, they robbed the U.P. train,
And split up in couples and started out again;
Joel Collins and his partner were overtaken soon;
With all their hard-earned money, they had to meet their doom.

Sam made it back to Texas, all right-side-up with care;
Rode into the town of Denton with all his friends to share.
Sam's life was short in Texas—three robberies he did do;
He robbed all the passengers, mail and express cars, too.

Sam had four companions—four bold and daring lads—
They were Underwood and Jackson, Joel Collins and Old Dad;
More bold and daring cowboys the Rangers never knew;
They run the Texas Rangers and whipped the boys in blue.

Sam had another companion, called "Arkansas" for short,
Was shot by a Texas Ranger by the name of Thomas Floyd;
Tom is a big six-footer and thinks he's mighty fly;
But I can tell you, boys, his racket: he's a deadbeat on the sly.

Jim Murphy was arrested and then released on bail;
He jumped his bond in Tyler and then took the train for Terrell.
But Major Jones had posted Jim, and that was all a stall;
'Twas only a plan to capture Sam before the coming fall.

Sam met his fate at Round Rock, July the twenty-first;
They filled poor Sam with rifle balls and emptied out his purse.
Poor Sam, he is a corpse now and six feet under clay,
And Jackson's in the bushes trying to get away.

Jim had borrowed Sam's good gold and didn't want to pay;
The only shot he saw was to give poor Sam away;
He sold out Sam and Barnes and left their friends to mourn;
Oh, what a scorching Jim will get when Gabriel blows his horn.

And so he sold out Sam and Barnes and left their friends to mourn;
Oh, what a scorching Jim will get when Gabriel blows his horn.
Perhaps he's gone to Heaven—there's none of us can tell;
But if I'm right in my surmise, he's gone right straight to Hell.

Travelin' Light

R. W. Hampton is a gifted songwriter and singer who makes his living as a working cowboy. I liked this song of his from the first time I heard him sing it. That was several years ago on a pack trip high in the San Juan Mountains of northern New Mexico. We had some memorable and fun times there. Those times, like this song, have become a part of my life.

Like most people, I'm drawn to songs that I feel I not only can sing well but can also identify with. I find the audience is more appreciative of a song I relate to than a song that might be popular just for the moment. I like songs from the heart, and it's especially satisfying when they are written by good friends like R. W.

TRAVELIN' LIGHT

R. W. Hampton

Today I quit my job, leave this city far behind;
I'm all through with trouble and strife.
Haven't got a thing to show for what I've done with my life,
But I'm not poor, I'm Travelin' Light.

Chorus:
I've got the blue sky above me,
A good pony 'tween my knees;
Everything I own I carry on my back,
That's all a cowboy ever needs.
I'm ridin' high, wide, and handsome again;
Jest like the wind, I'm Travelin' Light.

My heart belongs where a cowboy can roam,
Wild and free, now that's living right;
And to lay beneath the stars at night, wait for the moon to rise;
Jest like him, I'm Travelin' Light.

Chorus

Oh I'm heading west, never looking back,
I'll say so long to big city life;
I won't rein my pony in, till the feeling is right;
Adios, I'm Travelin' Light.

Chorus

Don meets up with R. W. Hampton and Alvin Crow in the high country of northern New Mexico.

To-day I quit my job, ___ leave this ci-ty far be-hind; ___ I'm all through

with trou-ble and strife. Have-n't got a thing to show ___ for what I've ___

___ done with my life, But I'm not poor, I'm Trav-el-in' Light.

Chorus

I've got the blue sky a-bove ___ me, A good po-ny 'tween my

knees; Ev-ery-thing I own I car-ry on my back,

That's all a cow-boy ev-er needs. I'm rid-in' high, ___ wide, and

hand-some a-gain; ___ Jest like the wind, I'm Trav-el-in' Light.

The Wandering Cowboy

I guess I haven't been looking hard enough, but I haven't found too many versions of this song. Its author also has eluded me.

This is one of those songs I've known a long time but never seem to sing unless someone reminds me of it. I have never seen a printed version with music, so the only tune I remember is a melody pretty close to "The Lone Star Trail." It fits the song, so who am I to differ?

THE WANDERING COWBOY

Traditional
Arrangement and Adaptation by Don Edwards

I am a wandering cowboy; from ranch to ranch I roam.
At every ranch, when welcome, I make myself at home.
Two years I worked for the Double L; one for the O Bar O;
Then drifted west from Texas to the plains of Mexico.

There I met up with a rancher who was lookin' for a hand.
When springtime greened the valleys, I was burnin' the Bar S brand;
I worked on through the summer, then early in the fall,
Over the distant ranges came that old familiar call.

Drifted out to Arizona to work for Uncle Bob,
A-tailin' for the weak ones on a winter's feedin' job.
But the ranch camp grew too lonely with never a rest or change,
So I saddled up one mornin' an' struck for a distant range.

One night in old Wyoming when the stars hung bright and low,
I lay in my tarp a-dreamin' of a far-off home rancho,
Where the cottonwood leaves are whisperin' in the evenin' soft 'n' low,
'Tis there my heart's a-turnin', and homeward I must go.

I've traveled lots of country—Nebraska's hills of sand,
Down through the Indian nation, and up the Rio Grande.
But now I'm tired of ramblin'; no longer will I roam
'Cause now my pony's grazin' on the rancho I call home.

C   G   C

I am a wan - d'ring cow - boy; from ranch to ranch I roam. At

F   C

ev - 'ry ranch, when wel - come, I make my - self at home. Two

F   C

years I worked for the Dou - ble L; one for the O Bar O; ___ Then

G   C

drift - ed west from Tex - as to the plains of Mex - i - co. ___

West of Yesterday

I can't classify myself in the singer-songwriter category 'cause I only write songs when the inspiration hits. So I'm not what you'd consider a good craftsman or authority on songwriting. I just sort of write what I feel.

Tom Mix was one of my all-time cowboy heroes. He wasn't a singer (professionally, at least), but he was a real cowboy and a pretty good poet. His later talking pictures were still being shown occasionally when I was a kid, and of course there was the Tom Mix radio show every week.

The inspiration for this song came from an article in *Frontier Times* titled "Tom Mix's Last Sundown," by Walt Coburn. The title came from two sources, one was from a *Los Angeles Times* publication called "West of Yesterday." The West of Yesterday—that was to be my very reason for existing, my soul and inspiration.

In the story, Sheriff Ed Echols and Tom Mix came to visit Walt at his place in Tucson, Arizona. They all fixed themselves a drink and rolled a smoke. Then Ed Echols and Tom Mix began telling yarns about their cowboyin' days and working for the 101 Ranch Wild West Show. Then Tom got to talking about his motion picture days and how ridiculous some of those scripts were, written by those dude Hollywood screenwriters, and how all they ever did was to increase the overhead of the five-reel pictures. All they ever did was talk, talk, talk, but none of them ever said anything. Every time Tom, with his firsthand knowledge of the West, would say anything, it was always squelched as being out of order. Sounds like the music business.

They fixed themselves another drink and went back to the porch to visit some more and to enjoy the quiet of the desert sunset. The distant mountains took on a purple haze, and only the call of the quail broke the evening silence. The mourning doves and kit foxes came to feed as the men said their good-byes until tomorrow. That tomorrow never came. Walt received a telephone call that Tom Mix had been killed in his car between Oracle Junction and Florence.

Walt was stunned by Tom's death, and he only wanted to be left alone with his grief and his thoughts of yesterday when Tom Mix was alive. He saddled his horse and rode off into the foothills, remembering what Tom did when he was feeling down—how he'd ride off alone for an hour or so in the saddle, and all his worries would be gone. Walt got to thinking about Tom's tragic death that day. In trying to make some sense out of it, he got to figuring how Tom was crowding sixty and was past the prime of his life. His movie career was over. Old age and being broke would have been his ultimate future. "Far worse things could have happened to Tom Mix than sudden death." Tom had seen his last sunset with his cowboy friends. He had heard the sounds of the quail and mourning doves in the hushed twilight. If Tom Mix had deliberately planned his passing, this place could have never been more fitting.

Tom Mix may be gone, but he'll never die in the nostalgic memories of the millions who loved him and the image he left behind. After reading this story, I wrote this song as a tribute to my hero Tom Mix.

WEST OF YESTERDAY

Don Edwards

In the evening's twilight, melancholy shadows stray
Down the trail of memories from West of Yesterday.
The night's a time for thinking back to days of long ago,
And my fav'rite cowboy hero, and that famous horse he rode.

Chorus:
They rode the open range across the silver screen,
Over sawdust trails, and purple sage, and in a young man's dreams.
Dreams don't last forever, but the memories never die
Out there West of Yesterday where Tom Mix will always ride.

I remember his last sundown as he watched that crimson desert sky.
Do you think he knew the mourning doves were singing their last good-bye?
Do you think he chose this place to die? Did he plan his destiny?
The answer's in the desert wind where his spirit still rides free.

Chorus:
He rides on Heaven's range beyond the mountain's purple haze,
Over stardust trails and golden clouds in that land of endless days;
For it's the place where dreams come true and memories come alive,
Out there West of Yesterday, Tom Mix will always ride.
Out there West of Yesterday, Tom Mix and Tony will always ride.

D   Em   C   A7   D

In the eve-ning's twi-light, __   mel-an-chol-y shad-ows stray   Down the trail of

Em   C   A7   D   D

mem - o - ries   from __ West of Yes-ter-day.   The night's a time for

Em   C   A7   D

think-ing __   back to days of long a - go,   And my fav-'rite cow-boy

Em   C   A7   D   D7   *Chorus*

he - ro, __   and that fa-mous horse he rode.   They

G   D

rode the o - pen range __   a - cross the sil - ver   screen, __   O - ver

E7   A7

saw - dust trails, __   and pur - ple sage, __   and in a young man's dreams. __

Em   C   A7   D

Dreams don't last for - ev - er, ___   but the mem-ories nev-er die

Em   C   A7   D

Out there West of Yes - ter - day   where Tom Mix will al-ways ride.

When I Was a Cowboy

Here is yet another song with a cowboy theme that is rooted in the blues idiom. There are many recordings of the song, and in most cases, it is credited to Leadbelly as being the author. In fact, the John A. Lomax text in *Cowboy Songs and Other Frontier Ballads,* the song is titled "Leadbelly's Chisholm Trail," whereas in Austin and Alta Fife's *Cowboy and Western Songs,* there are two texts but no credit to Leadbelly.

Leadbelly's version isn't cowboy at all. He never made any claims of being a cowboy, so I think he made up his lyrics to please the song collector. The lyrics in the Fife collection are much more authentic and might possibly have been written by a black trailhand. In his book *We Pointed Them North,* Teddy "Blue" Abbott included a similar type song sung by Ab Blocker's top Negro cowhand, John Henry, who was riding night guard on a Blocker herd while camped on the Cimarron River. According to Abbott, John Blocker was the greatest trail man who ever pointed a herd toward the North Star, and his brother Ab Blocker was the fastest driver on the trail.

> I'se gwine north with the
>   Blocker seven herd,
> And Mister Ab is a-movin'
>   like a bird, o-o-o-oh.

In my version of the song, I usually play it in an open G tuning with a slide on my 1926 Gibson Mastertone Guitar/Banjo. It's got a great, funky, old-time sound.

WHEN I WAS A COWBOY

"Leadbelly" Huddie Ledbetter
Arrangement and Adaptation by Don Edwards

When I was a cowboy out on the western plains,
When I was a cowboy out on the western plains,
I made a half a million pulling on the bridle reins.

Chorus:
Come a ki-yi-yippi, come a ti-yi-yippi yippi yea,
Come a ki-yi-yippi, come a ki-yi-yippi yippi yea.

Rode a silver-mounted saddle, got spurs and leggings too,
Rode a silver-mounted saddle, got spurs and leggings too;
They cost me fourteen dollar, the day that they were new.

Chorus

I had a little woman, and she was hard to please,
I had a little woman, and she was hard to please,
So I roped a streak o' lightning and drug it to my knees.

Chorus

When I left my girl's house, she was rocking in a rocking chair,
When I left my girl's house, she was rocking in a rocking chair,
"Po' western cowboy, please doncha leave me here."

Chorus

Good morning, young fellow, where would you like to go?
Good morning, young fellow, where would you like to go?
We'll go to punching cattle, way down in Mexico.

Chorus

Your grub, it is corn dodger and coffee black as ink,
Your grub, it is corn dodger and coffee black as ink;
The hard old alkali water ain't scarcely fit to drink.

Chorus

G
When I was a cow - boy _____ out on the west - ern

C7
plains, When I was a cow - boy _____ out on the west - ern

G   D7
plains, I made a half __ a mil - lion _____ pull-ing on the bri - dle reins. _

G   C   D7
Chorus
— Come a ki - yi - yip - pi, come a ti - yi - yip - pi yip - pi

G   C   D7   G
yea, Come a ki - yi - yip-pi, come a ki - yi - yip-pi yip-pi yea. _____

They wake you in the morning before the break of day,
They wake you in the morning before the break of day,
And send you on a circle a hundred miles away.

Chorus

When the bunkhouse catch on fire, and there ain't no water 'round,
When the bunkhouse catch on fire, and there ain't no water 'round,
Throw your war bag out the window; let the doggone shack burn down.

When You and I Were Young, Maggie

Cowboys didn't always sing range songs, and many of the old hands sang to tunes imported from the East whenever they could get wind of 'em. We sang as much about broken loves as we did breaking horses."—Will James

Another quote on the subject, this one from Jack Thorp: "A lot of singing on the range had nothing to do with cowboys as such. There were railroad songs, mountain, river and sticky-sweet sentimental ballads like 'Mollie Low,' 'Sweet Mollie Mine,' and 'My Little Georgia May.' Cowboys weren't always singing about 'little dogies' or 'give me a home where the buffalo roam.'"

"Maggie" was written in 1866 by George W. Johnson and James Austin Butterfield, an Englishman. This is one of these sticky-sweet type songs that Thorp mentioned when talking about songs the cowboys liked to sing. Songs like this never grow old; they're as good today as they were a hundred years ago.

I have heard other versions of the song with slightly different lyrics, which makes me think the song might have had some Irish influence. But nonetheless, this song was one of the favorites among the cowboys in the 1870s.

WHEN YOU AND I WERE YOUNG, MAGGIE

George W. Johnson and James Austin Butterfield

I wandered today to the hill, Maggie,
    to watch the scene below—
The creek and the old rusty mill, Maggie,
    where we sat in the long long ago.
The green grove is gone from the hill, Maggie,
    where the birds sang loud from the trees;
When I first said I loved only you, Maggie,
    and you said you loved only me.

Chorus:
But now we are aged and old, Maggie,
    the trials of life nearly done;
Let's sing of the days that are gone, Maggie,
    when you and I were young.

Our dreams, they have never come true, Maggie,
    our hopes, they never were to be
When I first said I loved only you, Maggie,
    and you said you loved only me.
The green grove is gone from the hill, Maggie,
    where first the wild flowers sprung;
The old rusty mill is now still, Maggie,
    since you and I were young.

Chorus

I wan-dered to-day to the hill, Mag-gie, ___ to watch the scene be-low ___

___ The creek and the old rust-y mill, Mag-gie, ___ where we

sat in the long long a - go. The green grove is gone from the

hill, Mag-gie, ___ where the birds sang loud from the trees; When I

first said I loved ___ on-ly you, ___ Mag-gie, ___ and you said you loved on-ly

Chorus

me. But now we are a-ged and old, Mag-gie, ___ the

trials of life near-ly done; Let's sing of the days ___ that are gone, ___

___ Mag-gie, ___ when you and ___ I ___ were young.

123

The Young Ranger

This was the first song I ever recorded, January 1964. It is based on the old ballad "The Dying Ranger." Dallas record producer Jim Ranne and I rewrote the lyrics and wrote a tune hoping that we might get the song played on the radio. It was my thinking that if we had a song that was reminiscent of Marty Robbins's gunfighter ballads that were very popular at the time, we might stand a chance. Well, the song never became a national success, but it did fairly well regionally. Remember, this was a time when radio disc jockeys knew the artists and the songs. They would listen to a new artist and at least give him or her a shot at a little radio play. These were also the days when a D.J. could play what he felt like playing—unlike today, where you have someone else dictating what you will and will not listen to. If it weren't for the small stations—both commercial and public—traditional music would never be heard. Sad but true.

Young Don Edwards gives a believable performance as a gunslinger at Six Flags Over Texas in 1961.

THE YOUNG RANGER

Traditional
Music by Don Edwards and Jim Ranne

The sun was slowly sinking and filled with brightest ray
By the Rio Grande in Texas where a wounded ranger lay
By a Texas border city beneath the southern sky;
Far away from his home, they laid him down to die.

The rangers gathered 'round him, his comrades in the fight;
A tear rolled down each manly cheek as he bid his last good night.
One tried and true commander was kneeling by his side
To stop the life blood flowing but in vain, in vain he tried.

It grieved his heart with pity when he knew it was too late,
The tall young Texas Ranger, death was to be his fate;
Up spoke the wounded ranger, "Don't weep no more for me,
And take good care of my sweetheart, she has no one, you see.

"A fair young girl, my sweetheart, she will see my face no more;
But in patience she is waiting by a lonely cottage door.
Come listen to me, comrades, and listen to my prayer
Who will be to her as brothers and shelter her with care?"

Then answered the weary rangers, they answered one and all,
"We will be to her as brothers till the last one of us fall."
One happy smile of pleasure o'er his face was spread;
In silence then they knew, the young ranger was dead.

The Zebra Dun

THE ZEBRA DUN
Traditional

Nobody loved a practical joke more than a cowboy. The rougher and more dangerous the joke, the more he enjoyed it, especially if a dude or a "greenhorn" was the main subject. But a true cowboy could "take it" if the joke backfired, as was the case in this cowboy poem that tells how every "educated feller" wasn't a plumb greenhorn.

"The Zebra Dun," or the "Educated Feller" as it is sometimes called, was first collected by cowpuncher and ballad hunter N. Howard "Jack" Thorp. This is another one of those traditional ballads that no one seems to know for sure who wrote it. Thorp said he first heard it in 1890. John Lomax was told the song might have been written by Negro Jake in the employ of John Z. Means of Valentine, Texas. In her wonderful song collection *Singing Cowboy*, Margaret Larkin mentioned that she had heard the song, but it was not about a zebra dun at all; it was about a dun-colored bronco with a Z Bar brand.

The tune I've given here is the only tune I've heard used. It's from an old Irish air "The Son of a Gambolier." Because of the popularity of this song most folks have concluded that every dun-colored horse is some kind of snakey, sage-tailed outlaw.

For those of you who have never seen or heard of a zebra dun horse, here is a brief description: the zebra dun is a light tan or dun color, with a brown or black mane and tail, a brown stripe running down its back, and zebra stripes circling the lower part of the legs. These markings were pretty common in mustangs in the early days but are quite rare today.

No matter what you call it, be it "The Zebra Dun," "Educated Feller," or whatever, this song is still a favorite among cowboys and around campfires.

We were camped out on the plains at the head of the Cimarron,
When along come a stranger, and he stopped to argue some;
He looked so very foolish that we began to look around;
We thought he was a greenhorn that just 'scaped from town.

We asked if he'd had breakfast, and he hadn't had a sniff;
We opened up the chuck box and told him help hisself.
He took a cup of coffee, some biscuits, and some beans,
And then begun to talk about the foreign kings and queens.

He talked about the Spanish War and fighting on the seas,
With guns as big as beef steers and ramrods big as trees;
He talked about ol' Paul Jones, a mean-fighting son of a gun;
Said he was the grittiest cuss that ever pulled a gun.

Such an educated feller, his thoughts just came in herds;
He 'stonished all us punchers with his jaw-breaking words.
He just kept on talking till he made the boys all sick,
And they begun to look around just how to play a trick.

He said he lost his job out upon the Santa Fe,
And he was going across the plains to strike the 7 D.
He didn't say how come it—just some trouble with the boss;
But he said he'd like to borrow a nice fat saddle horse.

This tickled all the boys to death; they laughed down in their sleeves,
Said that he could have a horse as fresh as he would please.
So Shorty grabbed the lasso and roped the Zebra Dun;
They led him to the stranger, and we waited for the fun.

Old Dunny was an outlaw that had grown so awful wild;
He could paw the white out of the moon every jump for a mile.
Old Dunny stood right still as if he didn't know,
Until he was saddled and ready for the go.

The stranger hit the saddle, and Old Dunny quit the earth;
He went straight up in the air for all that he was worth,
A-pitchin' and a-squealin' and having wall-eyed fits,
His hind feet perpendicular, his front ones in the bits.

We could see the tops of trees 'neath him every jump,
But the stranger, he was growed there just like a camel's hump.
The stranger sat upon him and curled his black mustache,
Just like a summer boarder waiting for his hash.

He thumped him in the shoulders and spurred him when he whirled;
He showed us flunky punchers, he's the wolf of this old world;
And when he had dismounted once again upon the ground,
We knew he was a thoroughbred and not a gent from town.

Chords: A E A

We were camped out on the plains at the head of the Cim - ar - ron, When a -

Chords: B7 E

long come a stran - ger, and he stopped to ar - gue some; He

Chords: A D A

looked so ver - y fool - ish that we be - gan to look a - round; We

Chords: E A

thought he was a green - horn that just 'scaped from town.

The boss was a-standing and watching all the show;
He walked right up to him and asked him not to go.
"If you can use the lasso like you rode the Zebra Dun,
Then you're the man I've looked for ever since the year of one."

Well he could use the lasso, and he didn't do it slow;
When the cattle, they stampeded, he was always on the go.
There's one thing and a sure thing I've learned since I was born:
Every educated feller ain't a plumb greenhorn.

DISCOGRAPHY

Happy Cowboy—produced by Larry Scott, Hollywood, California

America's Singing Cowboy—produced by Tommy Alsup, Dallas, Texas

Songs of the Cowboy—book/tape anthology of cowboy songs with guitar accompaniment

Guitars and Saddle Songs—book/tape anthology of cowboy songs with guitar accompaniment

Desert Nights and Cowtown Blues—produced by Don Edwards and Tom Morrell, Dallas, Texas (1990 Album of the Year, *Song of the West Magazine*)

Chant of the Wanderer—produced by Don Edwards and Tom Morrell, Dallas, Texas (1991 Western Heritage Wrangler Award for outstanding Traditional Western Music, National Cowboy Hall of Fame)

Songs of the Trail—Warner/Western Records, Nashville, Tennessee

Goin' Back to Texas—Warner/Western Records, Nashville, Tennessee

The Bard and the Balladeer—with Waddie Mitchell, produced by Don Edwards for Warner/Western Records, recorded live at Fort Worth, Texas

Recordings with other artists:

Other Voices, Other Rooms—Nancie Griffith, produced by Jim Rooney, Elektra Records (1993 Grammy Award for Best Contemporary Folk Album)

The Wild West—soundtrack from Time Warner, *The Wild West* TV miniseries, produced by John McEuen (1993 Western Heritage Wrangler Award for outstanding Traditional Western Music, National Cowboy Hall of Fame)

How the West Was Swung—Tom Morrell and The Time Warp Top Hands, produced by Tom Morrell, Priority Records, Dallas, Texas

Ridin' West, Vols. I and II— various artists, Crescendo Records, Sony

Buckaroo: Visions and Voices of the American Cowboy—book/CD set, various artists, edited by Hal Cannon, published by Simon and Schuster (1993 Western Heritage Wrangler Award, Cowboy Hall of Fame)

Cowboy Songs— Michael Martin Murphey, produced by Steve Gibson/MMM, Warner Brothers Records

Cowboy Christmas—Michael Martin Murphey, produced by Steve Gibson/MMM, Warner Brothers Records

A Christmas Tradition, Vol. III—various artists, Warner Brothers Records